Managing Safety the Systems Way

Managing Safety the Systems Way

Implementing BS OHSAS 18001:2007

David Smith, Geoff Hunt and Clive Green

Business
Information

First published in the UK in 1998 as *Managing Safety*; second edition in 2000; third edition
as *Managing Safety the Systems Way* in 2004; fourth edition in 2008
by
BSI
389 Chiswick High Road
London W4 4AL

Typeset in Optima by Monolith – www.monolith.uk.com
Printed in Great Britain by Berforts Group. www.berforts.com

British Library Cataloguing in Publication Data
A catalogue record for this book is available from the British Library

ISBN 978-0-580-50954-4

Contents

Foreword

Employees and society at large expect to be protected from any harm arising from the activities of organizations. Moreover, there is a good business case for effective management of occupational health and safety (OH&S) across all aspects of business activity, whether in the office, the workshop, the work site or as part of the general delivery of an organization's services. Quite apart from the regulatory and ethical issues, there are sound economic and commercial reasons for providing positive improvements to the overall quality of the work environment and for reducing work-related accidents, ill health and accidental damage to an organization's infrastructure, all of which can affect productivity.

Historically OH&S has been managed on a compliance basis – meeting the requirements of regulations and standards which, for the most part, have been introduced after a problem has reached significant levels. This approach will not succeed in the 21st century, particularly when dealing in global markets where different regulations and standards apply and working practices are ever-evolving to meet societal demands. It is also increasingly recognized that the compliance approach to managing OH&S does not, by itself, encourage continual improvement, which is the key driver for effectively managing OH&S in the workplace. The expectations of stakeholders are growing as innovation in the modern world allows us to create a safer workplace. The changing world also introduces new risks that make it hard for regulatory controls to keep pace. This is why the management system approach, using a risk base, is the soundest way to manage OH&S. While it is not possible to remove all risks in life, in the workplace these can be reduced to an acceptable level if not eliminated. The UK Health and Safety Executive (HSE) uses the approach described in its publication *Reducing Risks, Protecting People* [1] and this is the key to effective OH&S management. The aim is to identify risk in the workplace in order to eliminate unnecessary risk or implement effective control measures to reduce any risk that remains to an acceptable level and this includes risks not necessarily covered by current, local health and safety legislation. The approach taken in this publication is consistent with the direction given by the UK Health and Safety Commission's strategy, Revitalising Health and Safety, outlined in their free leaflet, *Leading health and safety at work – Leadership actions for directors and board members* [2].

With the new Corporate Manslaughter and Corporate Homicide Act 2007 being enacted in the UK, there is an even greater need for those directors and senior managers who were previously not committed to the effective implementation of OH&S systems to take note and act. The approach advocated within the two British standards described in the next paragraph, will help organizations meet the requirements placed upon them and enable them to show that they have put effective systems in place.

Organizations are now seeking ways of demonstrating to a wider audience that they are applying the principles of risk management to occupational health and safety. BS OHSAS 18001:2007 has been produced as a specification standard against which organizations can seek accredited certification. It is a consensus document supported by industry, commerce, practitioners, insurers and regulators. The standard is seen as one way of demonstrating the implementation of an effective OH&S management system as advocated originally by BS 8800:2004, the HSE's HSG65 [3] and the International Labour Office's *Guidelines on occupational health and safety management systems* [4]. BS OHSAS 18001, BS 8800, HSG65 and the ILO OSH guidelines are fundamentally the same in approach and the effective implementation of any one will also satisfy the other three.

The fourth edition of *Managing Safety the Systems Way* follows the publication of BS OHSAS 18001. Although the structure of previous editions is retained, it has been updated to include amendments and additional requirements from the new specification. It also includes a much improved approach in Chapter 2, 'Getting started' for those who are implementing a system with little formal arrangements currently in place. There have also been significant developments in the area of integrating management systems. The success of earlier editions gives testament to the effectiveness of the methodology it uses. The examples of fictitious organizations across a number of business sectors have also proved particularly helpful to some when implementing a new OH&S management system or developing an existing one.

Managing Safety the Systems Way is intended for organizations seeking practical guidance in delivering a cost-effective OH&S management system. It provides a structured approach for any organization wishing to implement an OH&S management system and will be particularly useful to small and medium-sized organizations and business units within larger corporate bodies that wish to develop a formal OH&S management system. Those organizations with existing OH&S management systems in place may also benefit from its guidance, especially in taking a risk-based approach.

This publication is designed to be helpful to those organizations seeking to integrate OH&S within an overall formal management system covering quality and/or environmental management. It is based on a Plan, Do, Check, Act (PDCA) approach used in management system standards, such as BS EN ISO 14001:2004. For those seeking to integrate their management systems, Chapter 11, which focuses on PAS 99:2006, *Specification of Common Management System Requirements as a Framework for Integration* [5], may be particularly helpful.

Managing Safety the Systems Way builds on the basic framework and principles of BS OHSAS 18001 and BS 8800 by providing practical advice, examples and sources of further information. It is not, however, intended to be a comprehensive guide to all aspects of OH&S and does not in any way alter or amend limitations on the use of BS OHSAS 18001. Readers are advised to consult both these documents for further background. Any definitions used also apply in this publication.

Adopting BS OHSAS 18001 and BS 8800 is not a legal requirement, nor will compliance with them confer immunity from legal obligation. BS 8800 is, however, identified in the *Management of Health and Safety at Work Regulations 1999. Approved Code of Practice and guidance* [6], Regulation 5, as one way of implementing an effective OH&S system.

The following model is based on the one used in BS OHSAS 18001 with the additional element, 'Initial status review', as found in BS 8800. The PDCA process is also a feature of the ILO OSH guideline document although there is a slight difference in order.

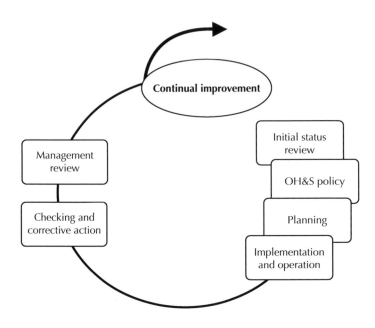

BS OHSAS 18001:2007 Model for a successful health and safety management system

1

Introduction

Since the Industrial Revolution in the UK over 200 years ago there has been an ever-increasing drive to improve the occupational health and safety arrangements of organizations. The approach in the past has mainly been through regulation. The laws passed were based on the suffering experienced by many in specific industries that necessitated an Act of Parliament to be passed to prevent a continuance of the circumstance that led to the hardship. This retrospective approach was laudable in its way but serious accidents or ill health problems had to occur before such laws were formulated. Some of this regulation was so prescriptive it brought its own problems and created other OH&S issues. Nowadays, the proactive approach is obviously preferred – let's prevent harm before it occurs to anyone.

Lord Robens, in his *Safety and Health at Work: Report of the Committee 1970–72* [7], published in 1972, recognized that the prescriptive regulatory approach could be a disincentive rather than being helpful in managing occupational health and safety:

> Our present system encourages rather too much reliance on state regulation and rather too little on personal responsibility and voluntary, self-generating effort.

> Regulations which lay down precise methods of compliance have an intrinsic rigidity and their details may be quickly overtaken by new technological developments. On the other hand, lack of precision creates uncertainty.
>
> As a result, much of the legislation appears irrelevant to the real, underlying problems.

In many ways, the more recent regulations have followed this thinking, the most significant in Europe probably being the Framework Directive of 1989. This led the UK to produce The Management of Health and Safety at Work Regulations in 1992, amended in 1999, requiring, in effect, the identification and control of occupational health and safety risks. There is now a greater need than ever before to be proactive in identifying those activities that might give rise to harm rather than waiting for a prescriptive requirement to be made on how to manage the risk.

The HSE guidance document HSG65, first published in 1991, is much revered and has been an invaluable tool in moving the 'management' of safety forward. Since then there have been a number of other approaches that have brought success. BS 8800, first published in 1996, encompassed much of the thinking in HSG65 and embraced other good guidance within a management system framework similar to that used by industry to manage other disciplines, e.g. BS EN ISO 9004 for quality and BS EN ISO 14004 for the environment. BS 8800 was revised in 2004 and is now seen as a very useful guide to good practice with respect to a system for managing OH&S. Its content in many ways is an improvement on HSG65 as it has taken on developments that have occurred since HSG65 was first published. Moreover, BS 8800 was written by industry, regulators, trade unions and trade organizations. It is recognized as practical good practice which could be realistically implemented across most organizations.

The need for an effective system has been emphasized by the new Corporate Manslaughter and Corporate Homicide Act 2007, which states:

(1) An organisation to which this section applies is guilty of an offence if the way in which its activities are managed or organised –
   (a) causes a person's death, and
   (b) amounts to a gross breach of a relevant duty of care owed by the organisation to the deceased.

The phrase 'the way in which its activities are managed or organised' points very much towards a management system for managing occupational health and safety. Top management and managers will need to demonstrate that they are meeting these requirements should they have to defend themselves against charges under this new Act.

BS 8800 was published as a 'guide' and as such it cannot be used for audit purposes. It also contained statements which were not applicable to all organizations. The pressure to have a standard that could be audited against, allowing accredited certification, led to the publication of OHSAS 18001 in 1999. The new version, BS OHSAS 18001:2007 has been adopted as a requirement standard. This specification is seen as providing a very good framework for implementing an effective and efficient system and allowing independent assessment of its effectiveness.

Managing Safety the Systems Way has been written to help those wishing to implement such a system. This approach will help those organizations wishing to demonstrate their commitment to preventing harm to workers and others who may be affected by the organization's activities – in other words those interested in going beyond a mechanical approach to just complying with relevant regulations and instead actively seeking to promote a healthy and safe working environment. The system being advocated here will show regulators, insurers and customers that the organization is managing OH&S in a way that encourages workers to work with management in being effective and productive, minimizing production loss and absenteeism. Obtaining 'buy-in' of the worker and the manager provides an opportunity to maintain the momentum of continual improvement in OH&S performance.

There have been other significant pressures on organizations, both large and small, from more unexpected sources. The London Stock Exchange published rules on corporate governance for listed companies called The Combined Code: Principles of good governance and code of best practice (now adopted by the Financial Reporting Council). This recognizes that the share value of a company is not only based on asset value but also on the success of the directors in managing all the strategic risks that the business faces, including OH&S. The UK government has extended this practice to the public sector, including higher education establishments.

- 140,000 reported workplace accidents
- 2.2 million people suffer work related illnesses resulting in 30 million lost working days
- 241 people killed at work

Source: Health & Safety Commission, October 2007

Any accident comes with a cost to the organization. The cost of occupational ill health is equally as important as accidents yet is often not given due recognition. Major accidents and claims for ill health and injury as well as damage to plant, equipment and property are costly both in the short term, due to production and delivery delays, and in the longer term through the loss of reputation caused by adverse publicity and the impact of legal enforcement. *The Combined Code on corporate governance* [8] affects other organizations besides listed companies because listed companies need to assure themselves that their suppliers, both in their trading practices and the supply of products and services, are not putting them at risk.

Governmental and stakeholder pressure has also led organizations in the private and public sector to focus on corporate social responsibility (CSR). OH&S is just one element but it is a key requirement that has to be addressed when delivering CSR. The pressure for CSR controls comes from the European Union. There are standards currently being developed by the International Organization for Standardization (ISO) and one has been produced by BSI. In the UK the 'Revitalising Health and Safety' initiative, a joint initiative by the UK government and the Health and Safety Commission, also sent a clear message to managers of organizations still not convinced about the need for an effective OH&S management system.

Finally, the UK Government announced in 2004 a new strategy that is a landmark in itself. This strategy is described in the HSE publication, *Reducing risks, protecting people: HSE's decision-making process.* The following statements from that publication recognize that the workplace can never be totally safe and that the aim should be to control the risks to an acceptable level yet not be over-prescriptive:

Our goal is not to have a risk free society but one where risk is properly appreciated, understood and managed.

We will become more robust in defending the reputation of the health and safety system against its detractors, those who are over zealous in its application and those who cannot recognize the appropriate balance between risks and benefits.

Importance of occupational health and safety management in smaller businesses

There is evidence that in the UK those in small businesses, i.e. those employing fewer than 50 people, are 40 per cent more likely to have an accident than their counterparts in larger organizations (with more than 1,000 employees). This is even more disturbing when considered alongside the trend of large organizations developing their businesses as smaller, autonomous operating units.

In some countries this divide is much greater. There is a clear need for organizations to improve their ability to manage OH&S safely rather than trying to understand the detail and requirements of all the regulations that may apply. As only about 40 per cent of organizations in the UK seem to have any sort of OH&S management arrangements, adoption of this approach would obviously go a long way towards improving overall OH&S performance.

The compliance approach is often too burdensome for small businesses. It is, however, recognized that many small businesses have quality systems such as BS EN ISO 9001 working effectively. Risk-based OH&S systems are just as easy to implement. Effective implementation of a system based on BS OHSAS 18001, BS 8800 and the ILO OSH guide should enable an organization to meet and even exceed 99 per cent of their compliance requirements.

Having implemented such a system it is often easier to identify the missing 1 per cent should it have been overlooked. The appeal of this management system approach is that an organization can embrace it within its business (risk) management system. A successful organization will then integrate OH&S into its day-to-day management arrangements, recognizing that there should be only one management system and style providing the necessary procedures and instructions. It will then continuously maintain its OH&S management programme, updating it and, most importantly, communicating it to those who are directly affected – employees, contractors, customers, clients, visitors and the public. Not only is communication with those closest to the organization essential, but evidence of successful OH&S management is now increasingly sought by other groups important to the well-being of the organization, such as investors, insurance companies, financial institutions and potential customers. For instance, one large pension investment group responsible for 4 per cent of the total investment in the UK stock market has instigated procedures to ensure its investments are restricted to companies that manage OH&S arrangements as well as other ethical issues.

By demonstrating a sound track record, organizations are able to show their commitment and sense of responsibility towards managing OH&S issues on an evolving basis. OH&S can be perceived as a serious drain on resources, offering little in the way of financial return. In practice, however, it has been shown that reducing accidents, occupational illness, equipment and plant damage, etc. will outweigh the costs of implementation, bringing additional benefits in the eyes of customers – for instance repeat orders in the knowledge that the organization is reliable. Improvements in performance indicators, such as the following, help to safeguard the welfare of employees and others, and at the same time benefit the financial performance of the organization:

- reduction in absenteeism;
- reductions in claims against the organization;
- improved insurance rating;
- absence of adverse publicity;
- improved production output;
- a positive response from existing and potential customers wanting to deal with an organization that has a successful OH&S track record and which is unlikely to be disrupted by costly accidents or plant shutdowns;
- lower risk of business interruptions.

The basic principles of management are common irrespective of the activity being managed. Many organizations have already achieved BS EN ISO 9001 status and are operating successful quality systems. With increasing awareness of the importance of managing environmental issues, organizations are also seeking certification to BS EN ISO 14001. BS OHSAS 18001 completes the trio of business management systems – quality, environmental and occupational health and safety.

Many organizations are now seeking to integrate their formal management systems. BS OHSAS 18001 and BS 8800 embody the principles upon which BS EN ISO 9001 and BS EN ISO 14001 are based and many commonalities exist between them. An OH&S management system based on BS OHSAS 18001/BS 8800 allows alignment or integration with these other systems. Comprehensive guidance is provided in Chapter 11 and Appendix 1 of this book on integrating such systems and organizations can choose for themselves the extent to which they wish to interface or integrate the three management systems. It is apparent that such an approach considerably reduces the duplication of paperwork and effort when three systems are operating within a single management system structure. It also avoids unnecessary bureaucracy, improves business focus and avoids potential conflicts.

Managing Safety the Systems Way explains how the various elements in developing an OH&S management system can be tackled, and how the system can be maintained as OH&S evolves, responding to internal and external influences.

Managing Safety the Systems Way uses six fictitious organizations to help readers with understanding – an office environment, an engineering workshop, a retail operation, a small construction company, a logistics operation and a company trading online. These very different work situations have been chosen to show the parallels that exist between them and how the same basic principles can be applied to all types of organizations and working environments. Clearly, effective OH&S management will not just simply happen. From the outset there needs to be commitment at the highest level and a proactive approach from the organization to addressing all OH&S issues. Management systems such as BS OHSAS 18001 and BS 8800 advance the challenge to organizations to attach the same level of importance to achieving high standards of OH&S as they do to other key business activities. There is only one guaranteed recipe for success: total commitment from managers and the organization by adopting a structured approach to identifying hazards in the workplace, evaluating and controlling work-related risks and developing a positive culture throughout the organization towards managing those risks.

How to use this book

For those wishing to build an OH&S management system, following this book through, page by page, allows a comprehensive system to be developed. To allow further flexibility for others with more particular needs, however, the book uses a combination of:

- key elements sections providing information on the key elements of BS OHSAS 18001;
- checklists giving a reference point to help organizations identify how their organization compares with BS OHSAS 18001 and BS 8800, and where they may need more detailed information;

- 'in detail' sections providing greater detail on what is needed to meet the guidance in BS OHSAS 18001 and BS 8800;
- 'in practice' sections showing how the system can be implemented in practice, mostly using the six fictitious organizations.

For those organizations with an OH&S system already in place

Many organizations will have an OH&S management system in place but they may either wish to check whether their existing system is adequate, or may already recognize that there are specific deficiencies that need to be addressed. In this case it may help to 'fast track' through the book by using the key elements sections and checklists to help identify how the organization compares and where more detailed information is needed. The 'in detail' sections can be referred to as necessary. (Note: Chapters 2 and 3 do not have separate 'in detail' sections but they do contain checklists; Chapter 2 also has 'in practice' sections.)

There is a self-assessment questionnaire in Appendix 2 that will help organizations to assess their present OH&S management system. It allows the benchmarking of current arrangements and charting of progress as their system becomes more effective.

For new starters who want to get the basics in place quickly

For those organizations with little or nothing in the way of an OH&S management system already in place, the process may seem daunting. There are no short cuts to success. The approach in this book, however, is such that it enables the new starter to identify the key elements that need to be addressed quickly. They can then proceed to the other elements later as the OH&S management system develops.

The key point to remember is that arrangements must be instituted to control the risks that are present. A good way to start is to address:

1. Getting started (see Chapter 2);
2. Risk assessment (see Chapter 6);
3. Planning (see Chapter 5);
4. Defining an OH&S policy (see Chapter 3);
5. Planning in detail (see Chapter 5).

For small organizations

The whole process of establishing an OH&S management system may appear overwhelming for a small organization, particularly when there are few obvious risks associated with its activities. The aim should be to address those OH&S issues present, managing them appropriately for the size and nature of the organization and the level of risk that exists.

Following a risk-based approach will help identify the priority issues that the organization needs to address. The initial status review and risk assessments are the key elements to concentrate on. It is, however, essential that the planning stage in this book is covered before a full risk assessment of the organization is carried out. The key elements sections in the other stages will then help in deciding the extent of the management system that will meet the organization's needs. In this case the way to proceed is:

1. Getting started (see Chapter 2);
2. Risk assessment (see Chapter 6);
3. Planning (see Chapter 5);
4. Defining an OH&S policy (see Chapter 3);
5. Key elements sections of the remaining stages.

Background to the case studies

To show how implementing an OH&S management system might work in practice, six fictitious organizations have been used as case studies. Any resemblance to actual organizations is purely coincidental, though the issues identified may be common to many.

The background to each organization is given as follows and the examples relating to each case study throughout the book can be identified easily by the logo in the margin. The examples and the approach have many features that will be common to all organizations, although there will always be some uniqueness about an individual organization's situation.

Floggitt & Leggit (F&L)

Introduction

F&L is a 17-strong firm of accountants, established in 1985 by four partners who previously practised separately. Throughout the late 1980s it expanded rapidly to become a firmly established business serving the UK and Europe. F&L have recently moved from old-fashioned offices to a modern, designer-built, two-storey office suite in a business development park.

F&L's partners have travelled a long way since the early days when health and safety didn't feature high on their agenda. Even as the new partnership developed, health and safety legislation was never thought to be particularly applicable. One partner had remarked, 'Offices aren't dangerous places and you don't need a written safety policy if there are less than five employees, so where's the harm?'

Implementing an OH&S management system

F&L's move to new offices brought an immediate recognition that even small businesses have some OH&S responsibility. The day before the official hand-over took place, a window cleaner fell from a ladder and broke an ankle – not the best start in a new place of work for an organization with a dynamic image. It also raised the question of liability – if the accident had occurred while F&L were tenants in the building, they might have been faced with a potential claim for damages. F&L's response to this event was to ask what precisely it should do as an organization taking responsibility for the health and safety of its staff, visitors and contractors.

Where does an organization in a relatively safe environment begin? The Health and Safety at Work etc. Act 1974 (HASWA) is the core of UK health and safety legislation and, as an enabling Act, has led to the development of new and modern regulations tailored to meet the needs of all industries. F&L clearly had to review its existing position with respect to OH&S. As there was no interest in seeking management system certification in the foreseeable future, BS 8800 provided the vehicle to establish effective arrangements to control its OH&S risks and to assure clients and insurers that it had a system in place meeting the requirements of BS OHSAS 18001.

In the 21st century, F&L is developing its international business, increasing working outside of the UK in the global marketplace. Hence F&L wants to ensure that its OH&S management principles adequately protect its staff when travelling and working overseas.

 ## Unbespoke Engineering (UE)

Introduction

UE is an established engineering organization tracing its roots back to World War I when it began manufacturing rivets, nuts and bolts for war production. The early premises, two small wooden shacks, have since developed into a five-hectare site with 83 employees, manufacturing precision gear mechanisms for the motor trade and high quality fasteners. Raw material is sent to the site for conversion into the finished product before being transported to a predominantly UK and European market.

The business activity is clearly divided into two categories: clerical/managerial support and manufacturing. The manufacturing side involves the use of precision engineering tooling and is undergoing a programme of replacement, modernization and computerization. The plant facilities are relatively modern and have been reasonably maintained.

OH&S matters are managed through a human resources manager who has received current training in fire and first aid safety and has a safety certificate issued by a local college. The duties are cascaded through middle management to three business managers with no OH&S background who are responsible for the manufacture and despatch of final products. The clerical function is managed through the HR Department. Basic OH&S compliance is clearly evident but is not organized or formally managed. UE's OH&S record is good, as far as records indicate, and there has not been a visit by the Health and Safety Executive (HSE) for some eight years.

Implementing an OH&S management system

UE's approach was initiated following the successful achievement of BS EN ISO 9001 compliance. UE was increasingly facing probing questions from its customers on every aspect of business performance – quality, health and safety and environmental policy. Pre-qualification tenders had exposed the lack of a robust occupational health and safety management system.

Some companies in its sector had already sought or were seeking certification to BS OHSAS 18001 for business credibility reasons and this provided the perfect vehicle for UE to look at how OH&S was being managed and how it could be improved. There was a solid foundation to build upon; clearly something was being done right, which was evident in the attention to detail UE instilled throughout its operations. Precision engineering requires attention to detail, slowly learnt, with pride in the finished product. The inherent discipline of the workforce would enable UE to quickly grasp the requirements of BS OHSAS 18001 and maintain them in practice.

UE's management was initially reluctant to embrace BS OHSAS 18001, which it saw as another expensive, time-consuming exercise that would distract from production. The review of their existing arrangements changed that view – it revealed what UE had to do to meet the plethora of modern health and safety legislation and to satisfy the demands of its customers.

The adoption of BS EN ISO 9001 had helped to formalize UE's management system arrangements and had strengthened its procedures and documentation; it therefore seemed an ideal platform to build on. BS OHSAS 18001 would be a valuable tool in helping the organization move forward to meet the demands of the 21st century.

There was, however, an unexpected problem area. UE was very proud of its registration to BS EN ISO 9001, seeing it as a vehicle for improving the management of the business and not just a paperwork exercise to gain a certificate on the wall. It came as a surprise that their system was not robust enough to integrate OH&S as it stood. The main problem was that the scope of its registration to BS EN ISO 9001 was very narrow, focusing on the manufacturing element. UE realized it would have to expand the scope of the current system to all areas of its operations. It also became conscious that the management of OH&S was risk-based and needed a different emphasis to its current quality approach. Having recognized these important differences, UE found there were significant opportunities for using common systems and that the current arrangements for managing quality only needed expanding or modifying slightly in order to embrace the needs of BS OHSAS 18001.

As UE has expanded, it has embraced modern engineering technologies. This has brought new risks as previous engineering practice has evolved. In the 21st century, computerization has replaced a lot of the old methodologies and removed hazards completely but in their place has come the potential for repetitive strain injury and computer software speeds that can put an operator under stress trying to keep pace with production.

Low Cost Discount (LCD)

Introduction

LCD has been trading since 1979, supplying a full range of cut-price food and household products. It occupies a single-storey, 200,000 square metre store on a shopping estate, sharing a common car park with 18 other traders. It has 30 full-time employees supported by 25 part-time or temporary staff brought in as needed. Staff turnover is quite high and 80 per cent are female. LCD is very aware of its responsibility to customers but has a poor record of minor accidents amongst staff, particularly in the warehouse area.

OH&S is the Store Manager's responsibility, supported by two assistants, none of whom has received any formal training. The local environmental health officer visits the store every four to five years. The most recent visit identified major failings and non-compliance with current OH&S legislation.

Implementing an OH&S management system

The organizational requirements of LCD are different from F&L and UE, demanding closer control and management.

Staffing arrangements involving significant numbers of temporary and part-time staff mean it is more difficult to ensure they are adequately trained and kept aware of OH&S issues. LCD's trade also involves the public, which requires continual attention. The supply of food to the public is a further issue, requiring compliance with strict food safety and hygiene legislation. LCD realized that, in order to remain in business, immediate action was required. It appointed one assistant manager with full responsibility for OH&S and BS 8800 was chosen as the vehicle to embrace OH&S arrangements in a formal management system.

LCD saw opportunities and benefits in integrating its management of hygiene requirements and OH&S. Both issues were likely to impact on employees and the public, one way or another, and it was necessary to manage this area of its business more effectively. With the continuing need for training, it was seen that OH&S could be conveniently accommodated within the general training arrangements already in place.

As LCD has developed, it has become increasingly aware of it responsibilities for ensuring the OH&S of its customers. It was recognized that injuries to customers could result in expensive litigation claims and loss of reputation, both of which could be expensive to LCD.

▰▰▰ Bilt & Clapse (B&C)

Introduction

B&C is a medium-sized construction company with 22 management and administrative staff, 173 tradesmen employees and a subcontract workforce of a further 220 permanent contractors who can be engaged as and when conditions dictate. This flexibility enables the company to be keenly competitive while at the same time undertaking significant construction projects. Throughout the 1990s B&C grew strongly and, being a construction organization, had come to accept that it would always have its share of accidents and incidents, the cost of which were written into tender fees.

In 1994 the HSE issued The Construction (Design and Management) Regulations (CDM) and followed this up in 1996 with the Construction (Health, Safety and Welfare) Regulations, both now incorporated into the CDM Regulations 2007. The impact on B&C came following a breach of the CDM Regulations with the collapse of a tower crane while the company was undertaking work to modify a power plant. Although eventually no blame was apportioned to B&C, the company was now unable to give positive answers in potential client pre-qualification questionnaires that would enable it to undertake the more prestigious construction contracts, particularly within the railway industry.

This incident was the catalyst that led to the Safety Officer and Commercial Director reporting to the board that B&C could soon begin to have difficulty in getting the work it wanted. Further, unless the company demonstrably improved its OH&S reputation, its traditional customer base could also be reduced.

Implementing an OH&S management system

B&C had never addressed the requirements of quality assurance or considered what environmental impact its activities might have. With the acceptance that the absence of a robust OH&S management system could ultimately lead to the failure of the company, however, the board made a commitment to ensure that B&C would meet these new demands being placed on organizations to become accountable for their actions.

The initial decision was to appoint a manager with experience in implementing management systems and to set a target for achieving BS EN ISO 9001 compliance within a six-month time frame. In addition, the newly appointed Quality Assurance Manager would assist the Safety Officer in implementing the various elements of BS OHSAS 18001 and to begin meeting the environmental management requirements of BS EN ISO 14001. A timescale for achieving full compliance and certification to BS OHSAS 18001 would be decided after the findings of an initial status review were reported and the extent of the work required could be quantified. A further and more far-reaching decision was that B&C would move towards a fully integrated OH&S quality and environmental management system as the most cost-effective way forward in the longer term.

In 2007, B&C had to face the challenge of the new Construction (Design and Management) Regulations, which came into force in April of that year. Now they also have a more multilingual workforce as the European Union market has opened up. Consequently, as well as ensuring the OH&S of its workforce and implementation of the 2007 regulations, B&C also has to ensure that its employees have a clear understanding of the process of implementation.

YumYumInMyTum (YYIMT.com)

Introduction

YYIMT was formed in 1999 with a workforce of 12 operating from new offices situated in a business park. It uses the Internet to trade in a wide and unique range of exclusive and exotic handmade sweets, cakes and other specialist confectionery made by a network of small independent manufacturers located around the UK. Its business is based on providing specialist shops and chain stores with supplies of fresh products through an independent delivery service. In addition, it provides a mail order service to home-based customers with all marketing and ordering carried out on the Internet.

YYIMT takes on the marketing and distribution roles for the manufacturers and has no direct manufacturing or storage facilities. From the outset it recognized an overall need to comply with all relevant OH&S and environmental legislation and realized that, as a food distributor, quality assurance would also be of prime importance. More specifically, however, the evidence among some of its IT operators of repetitive strain injury (RSI) from past employment, together with the general strength of food hygiene and health and safety legislation, meant there was a clear need for robust OH&S arrangements.

In addition, more investors representing pension investment portfolios were insistent on only dealing with companies that were operating sound, ethical, environmental and health and safety policies. This source of investment was seen as being important to YYIMT in the future and the company needed to be able to demonstrate its commitment to OH&S.

Implementing an OH&S management system

YYIMT decided to prepare for compliance before the organization was actually trading. This was achieved by identifying which operations would be carried out within the office complex to keep the operation functioning, as well as identifying the specific activities of the trading side. In addition, YYIMT wanted to ensure that it was trading with like-minded organizations and undertook to employ an ethical trading policy using only suppliers and contractors who were as equally committed as YYIMT. Consequently, it was looking for its confectionery suppliers and delivery organizations to be working towards compliance with BS OHSAS 18001 and the requirements of BS EN ISO 9001 and BS EN ISO 14001, if they did not already have them in place.

As YYIMT has evolved it has moved increasingly to operate a home-working regime for its teleworkers. While this has brought about improvements to the work–life balance, it has necessitated the need to ensure that home-workers have a suitable working environment which is OH&S compliant.

Heave and Haul (H&H)

Introduction

H&H was created from a family road haulage company transporting cattle to abattoirs. It now operates with a fleet of fixed and articulated wheelbase vehicles from five main hubs across the UK. In addition, H&H provides a network of local delivery services for a distribution-only wholesaler supplying perishable foodstuff. The core road haulage business operates across the boundaries of the extended European Union and familiarity and understanding of local and national health and safety issues is essential to the smooth running of the operation. In the UK, maintaining a reliable and prompt delivery service during predominantly unsociable hours presents an ever-present major risk challenge to H&H. The company therefore recognized that an effective OH&S management system was essential to its developing business.

Implementing an OH&S management system

To establish compliance with BS OHSAS 18001, H&H set up separate task forces to deliver it in the two distinct arms of its business, using the sound guidance given in BS 8800. A management group was also set up to monitor consistency across the two task forces as well as establish the BS 8800 approach in the business support areas – garaging, administration, etc. Although certification to BS OHSAS 18001 was an option, the company recognized the need to take on the principles given in the annexes of BS 8800, particularly with respect to culture and accident investigation. The latter was seen as being of particular importance in an industry that is high risk.

H&H's longer-term aim is for eventual integration with BS EN ISO 9001 and BS EN ISO 14001. H&H recognizes that to achieve and maintain compliance with BS 8800, it needs to ensure its business partners and suppliers are equally committed.

For H&H the 21st century has brought new hazards to its agriculture industry activity, with the need for biohazard controls to ensure the potential spread of infection or transmitted disease in agricultural herds is minimized.

2

Getting started – Initial status review

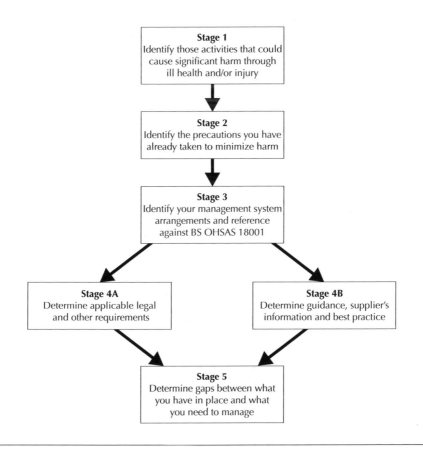

Stage 1
Identify those activities that could cause significant harm through ill health and/or injury

Stage 2
Identify the precautions you have already taken to minimize harm

Stage 3
Identify your management system arrangements and reference against BS OHSAS 18001

Stage 4A
Determine applicable legal and other requirements

Stage 4B
Determine guidance, supplier's information and best practice

Stage 5
Determine gaps between what you have in place and what you need to manage

In brief

If you do not already have a well-developed OH&S system – don't worry. It's time to get started using a simple step-by-step approach for implementing a system. It asks an organization to identify its 'problems' and what it has done to mitigate them. It asks them what they should be doing to meet legal requirements and guidance, and what gaps exist in their existing OH&S management system arrangements.

For any organization to either establish a new OH&S management system or develop an existing one, the first and most important step is to carry out a review of the arrangements and procedures already in place for controlling the risks. This process will provide established organizations with information on the scope, adequacy and degree of implementation of an existing management system and, particularly, where it stands in managing risk. For a newly established organization, an initial status review (ISR) serves to determine what arrangements are needed to ensure effective OH&S management functions and the statutory obligations it has to meet. This process of self-assessment essentially answers the question: precisely where is the organization now in managing OH&S issues and/or where does it need to be? It is a key step and identifies what information needs to be gathered and considered when establishing the OH&S system.

BS OHSAS 18001 does not specifically require an ISR to be carried out. OHSAS 18002, however, recognizes the need for an ISR in the case of an organization with limited OH&S management in place, to establish its current position. In addition, the ISR provides the starting point for the development and implementation of the management system process. Carrying out an ISR may, at first sight, seem an onerous task. Most organizations soon find, however, that the process demonstrates that OH&S is already part of their management arrangements. What has rarely been done is to assess its relevance against all aspects of business risk and to determine statutory obligations.

An ISR should always be undertaken by a competent person familiar with understanding and determining risks as well as identifying the legislation applicable to managing risks. They will need to engage in dialogue with all parts of the organization's operations to understand the services and products it provides and even the direction it intends to go, as part of the organization's evolution.

In the UK, since 1974, all 'persons at work', whether employers, employees or the self-employed, with the exception of domestic servants in a private household, have been covered by The Health and Safety at Work etc. Act 1974 (HASWA). This legislation additionally covers the health, safety and welfare of the general public, contractors and any person or persons who may be affected by an organization's activities. There is a similar requirement for protecting those affected by the organization's activities within the EU and in many other parts of the world.

All organizations, whether small, medium or large, will normally be operating some kind of safety management system. This may be unsophisticated and may not be totally compliant with current health and safety legislation but it will be there. It may have evolved as a result of an accident, a visit by the health and safety inspector or other regulatory body, or as a result of the experience and common sense of those working for the organization. In many cases, the safety management system may not be working as well as it should and, perhaps most importantly, not moving forward in response to business experience and development and changes in legislation. While there may be systems in place to prevent or reduce accidents, it is less likely that similar controls are in place for reducing occupational health problems, for example hearing loss, back problems or acute or chronic ill health from chemical exposure, for which the risk factors are often not as apparent as those presenting a clearly unsafe situation in terms of potential accidents. The ISR helps organizations find out:

- where they are now in managing OH&S issues;
- what help and information are available from internal and outside sources;
- what needs to be done to meet the organization's OH&S obligations;
- which of this is relevant to the organization;
- how the organization shapes up to meeting the core elements of the organization's OHSAS 18001 system.

Stage 1 – Identify activities that could cause significant harm through ill health and/or injury

To satisfy the requirements of the initial status review organizations will need to identify those activities that could result in harm. There are areas of activity that are well regulated but caution should be exercised when it comes to focusing immediately on those areas that the organization is well aware of, where there are specific requirements which it is already managing well. There are many activities that may cause harm where there may not be well-defined regulations (such as stress, for instance) or guidance. Emerging technologies may well bring new hazards to the workplace that pose an unacceptable risk. These need to be managed rather than waiting for regulation to be introduced. The approach needs to be one where the person responsible for this review steps back and considers the bigger picture, identifying those hazards that exist which are not necessarily regulated by specific legislation.

Those new to health and safety will no doubt find trying to read and understand the OH&S law a very onerous and time-consuming task. By contrast, identifying those activities that may cause unacceptable harm may well be a much easier approach. Identifying the hazards, determining the risks and putting in effective controls is likely to allow the organization to meet and/or exceed 99 per cent of the legal requirements it is obliged to comply with. Moreover, it may be possible to achieve this in a relatively short time compared with trying to analyse and understand all the legal requirements.

The following checklist details some of the potential sources for harm that are applicable to many organizations. A tick box has been provided to identify those that apply to the organization concerned (1) and those that have been addressed (2). A more comprehensive approach is provided in Chapter 6.

CHECKLIST: Hazard identification, risk assessment and risk controls

1	2	
❑	❑	Slips/falls on the level;
❑	❑	Falls of persons from heights;
❑	❑	Falls of tools, materials, etc., from heights;

☐	☐	Inadequate headroom;
☐	☐	Manual lifting/handling of tools, materials, etc.;
☐	☐	Hazards from plant and machinery associated with assembly, commissioning, operation, maintenance, modification, repair or dismantling;
☐	☐	Vehicle hazards, covering both site transport and travel by road (affecting personnel and other vehicles);
☐	☐	Fire, explosion and natural disasters;
☐	☐	Substances that may be inhaled;
☐	☐	Substances or agents that may damage the eye;
☐	☐	Substances that may cause harm by coming into contact with, or being absorbed through the skin;
☐	☐	Substances that may cause harm by being ingested, i.e. entering the body via the mouth;
☐	☐	Substances that may be injected by a needle or under pressure through broken skin;
☐	☐	Harmful energies, e.g. electricity, radiation, noise, vibration;
☐	☐	Work-related upper limb disorders resulting from frequently repeated tasks;
☐	☐	Inadequate thermal environment, e.g. too hot, too cold, extreme variations in temperature;
☐	☐	Lighting levels (adequacy for tasks or emergencies);
☐	☐	Slippery, uneven ground/surfaces;
☐	☐	Inadequate guard rails or hand rails on stairs;
☐	☐	Contractors' activities;
☐	☐	Violence to staff;
☐	☐	Terrorist activity;
☐	☐	Stress from work pressures, unrealistic deadlines, etc.;
☐	☐	Physical suitability of employees (health, fitness, etc.).

In practice

All the case study organizations found that many of the potential sources for harm listed applied to them. Although their first attempt at identifying all the hazards and evaluating the risks may not have been comprehensive, it gave them all a sound basis for progressing and moving to a more comprehensive approach (see Chapter 6). This enabled them to complete the exercise within a short space of time (after completing the 'getting started' stage of the process).

F&L

The ISR for F&L was broken into three elements representing business delivery.

1. Core office environment risks:
   - fire and terrorist threat;
   - first aid – contact with body fluids;
   - managing and selecting contractors;
   - manual handling, e.g. boxes and other office supplies, water dispensers;
   - slips, trips and falls;
   - staff consultations;
   - working with display screen equipment, VDUs.
2. Office location risks:
   - responsibility under The Workplace (Health, Safety and Welfare) Regulations 1992, e.g. decoration, lighting, sanitation provisions;
   - electricity – hard wiring and portable equipment;
   - maintaining and using pressure systems – heating, boilers, etc.;
   - chemicals – office and contractor;
   - disabled persons – employees and visitors.
3. Business environment risks:
   - driving and travelling long distances with limited rest periods;
   - use of mobile telephones;
   - violence – from the public, road rage.

F&L's business structure has the nucleus of a 'suitable and sufficient' health and safety management system. What was lacking was the recognition of all hazards and risks that existed across its working environments both within the confines of the office and outside it, as well as the ongoing control needed over them.

This was demonstrated by the fact that, while F&L had every piece of electrical equipment checked each year, its health and safety policy was last reviewed over 10 years ago and the hard wiring to the building and services had never been tested since they moved into the building.

The ISR enabled F&L to determine its risk exposure and prioritize the major risks to enable them to be addressed as a matter of urgency.

As F&L grows, each new activity and environment will be reviewed against legislation and best practice, any new risks identified, and control procedures developed and implemented before harm can occur.

UE

The ISR for UE identified three areas of risk management for business delivery.

1. Core business risks – these address the UE business environment:
   - fire and terrorist threat;
   - first aid – contact with body fluids;
   - manual handling, e.g. office and workshop deliveries;
   - selecting and managing contractors;
   - slips, trips and falls;
   - staff consultations;
   - working with display screen equipment, VDUs.
2. Specific office and workshop risks:
   - chemicals – office and workshop materials;
   - disabled persons – employees and visitors;
   - electricity – hard wiring and portable equipment;
   - emergency maintenance;
   - first aid – contact with body fluids;
   - food and canteen hygiene management – UE uses an employee canteen to provide 24-hour services;
   - working with machinery and equipment;
   - machine tool maintenance and management;
   - maintaining and using pressure systems – heating, boilers, etc.;
   - planned preventative maintenance;

- responsibility under The Workplace (Health, Safety and Welfare) Regulations 1992, e.g. decoration, lighting, sanitation provisions;
- the use and storage of flammable solvents, e.g. petrol, white spirit – UE uses solvents for cleaning and painting.

3. Business environment risks:
   - driving – visiting clients and deliveries;
   - manual handling – deliveries;
   - use of mobile telephones;
   - violence – from the public, road rage.

UE's operations involve considerable manual labour and an extensive infrastructure to support the business – warehouse, canteen facilities, etc. There is a greater than average incidence of hazards and an increased need to ensure adequate supervision and training of the workforce. UE's manufacturing base requires strong management control over all its operations. To prevent incidents occurring, OH&S management will require the continuous involvement of all staff. In addition, UE has a recognized trade union and, as such, has to establish and implement structured consultation processes on OH&S matters with its employees.

 ## LCD

The ISR for LCD was based on the management of risks in two areas of business delivery.

1. Core business risks – in the LCD business environment:
   - fire and terrorist threat;
   - first aid – contact with body fluids;
   - manual handling, e.g. office and workshop deliveries;
   - slips, trips and falls;
   - working with display screen equipment, VDUs.
2. Specific office, warehouse, premises and shop floor location risks:
   - applying first aid;
   - canteen hygiene management;

- chemicals – office and shop floor materials;
- disabled people – employees and visitors;
- driving – van deliveries to customers;
- electricity – hard wiring and portable equipment;
- maintaining and using pressure systems – heating, boilers, etc.;
- responsibility under The Workplace (Health, Safety and Welfare) Regulations 1992, e.g. decoration, lighting, sanitation provisions;
- use of mobile telephones;
- violence – from the public, road rage;
- working at night.

LCD has the additional responsibility of interfacing with the public and visitors, e.g. customers and delivery people. Its operation involves rapid set-up and turnover, requiring the safe operation of simple tasks using semi-skilled labour. A significant amount of work involves shelf stacking both at night, during unsocial hours, and when the store is open to shoppers. This provides additional risks.

While it had recognized its responsibilities on the retail side (food hygiene, first aid and fire precautions), LCD had given little attention to the support side – warehouse, traffic routes and staff training (especially part-time staff).

▦ B&C

The ISR for B&C was based on the management of risks in two areas of business delivery.

1. Core business risks in the B&C business environment – office location and B&C work premises:
   - fire and terrorist threat;
   - first aid – contact with body fluids;
   - forklift truck driving;
   - manual handling, e.g. office and work premises deliveries;
   - slips, trips and falls;
   - working with display screen equipment, VDUs.

2. Business delivery – work site risks:
   - chemicals – cement, etc.;
   - driving;
   - fire – flammable materials and bomb threats;
   - first aid – contact with body fluids;
   - managing contractors;
   - manual handling, e.g. office and site deliveries;
   - public control;
   - scaffolding erection and management;
   - site management;
   - slips, trips and falls;
   - specific task/skills competencies – Construction Skills Certification Scheme (CSCS) card compliance;
   - structure collapse;
   - use of machine and hand tools;
   - weather conditions – heat (sunburn), cold, wetness, etc.;
   - working at height;
   - working with display screen equipment, VDUs.

B&C's operations frequently mean that it has to work at a client's site or premises. It also has its own office and yard sites for which it is responsible and relies on significant periods of driving time between its own premises and worksites for delivery purposes etc.

As a builder, B&C also has specific responsibility under the CDM regulations when acting as a principal contractor and designer.

 ## YYIMT

In the case of YYIMT.com, the ISR only applied to a single area of business delivery.

1. Core business risks in the YYIMT business environment – office and work premises:

- fire and terrorist threat;
- manual handling, e.g. office and work premises deliveries;
- slips, trips and falls;
- working with display screen equipment, VDUs;
- first aid – contact with body fluids;
- electricity;
- managing contractors.

The business of YYIMT.com means that there is no direct interface with clients and customers, as these are managed electronically.

By planning in advance, YYIMT was able to ensure that, as far as was reasonably practicable, all of its OH&S responsibilities were being addressed. To ensure that risk is managed within the business, however, rigorous review processes are needed to monitor risk management and identify any additional risks it may have to face.

H&H

The H&H ISR was based on the management of risks in three areas of business delivery.

1. Core business risks in the H&H business environment – office premises:
   - fire and terrorist threat;
   - manual handling, e.g. office and work premises deliveries;
   - slips, trips and falls;
   - working with display screen equipment, VDUs;
   - first aid – contact with body fluids.
2. Business delivery – yard sites:
   - fire and terrorist threat;
   - manual handling, e.g. office and site deliveries;
   - slips, trips and falls;
   - working with display screen equipment, VDUs;
   - first aid – contact with body fluids;

- forklift truck driving;
- noise;
- biological hazards from animal wastes;
- chemicals – vehicle cleaning and refuelling;
- vehicle movements.
3. Business delivery – vehicle risks:
    - driving – other motorists and driving laws and conditions in other countries;
    - road rage – other motorists;
    - stress – meeting programme deliveries, e.g. ferry timetables;
    - tiredness – excessive hours and night driving.

Stage 2 – Identify the precautions already taken to minimize harm

This is where the organization identifies what is currently in place and is working satisfactorily. It will almost certainly be found that:

- machinery and equipment has been provided with guards and systems to prevent injury;
- guidance has been provided that has been adopted by employees on safe working practices;
- employees have adopted safe working procedures on the basis of previous employment or training;
- managers/supervisors have implemented some form of control to prevent a recurrence of an experience that caused harm or nearly caused harm (i.e. a near miss) at some time in the past;
- resources have been provided for certain precautionary measures (e.g. training, fire extinguishers).

Such information and solutions should be considered at Stage 4.

From the outset, all organizations have to establish at least some ground rules for the health, safety and welfare of staff and for the security and safety of their various activities. Very few operations are conceived without some regard for health and safety criteria. This may involve selecting a particular course of events or actions to eliminate risk, by reducing the risk if a particular course of events or actions occurs or by choosing to use particular, safer materials instead of others with known hazards.

The following checklist shows some of the health and safety aspects applying to organizations that should be covered by documented procedures. This list is not exhaustive and a tick box is provided for organizations to identify those that are in place or being introduced (1), may apply (2) or are irrelevant (3).

CHECKLIST: Existing OH&S information, guidance, etc. in your organization

1	2	3	
☐	☐	☐	Accident/incident/occupational ill health/near miss reporting and investigation;
☐	☐	☐	Alcohol and substance misuse testing and screening;
☐	☐	☐	Audits (OH&S);
☐	☐	☐	Cold environments (refrigeration);
☐	☐	☐	Communicating information – staff, contractors and others;
☐	☐	☐	Compressed air use;
☐	☐	☐	Confined working (permit to work);
☐	☐	☐	Contractor deliveries;
☐	☐	☐	Contractor services – selection based on OH&S skills and competencies;
☐	☐	☐	Management of contractors and visitors to offices and work sites;
☐	☐	☐	Management of substances hazardous to health;
☐	☐	☐	Management of substances hazardous to health;
☐	☐	☐	Display screen equipment (VDUs) – operation and use;
☐	☐	☐	Driving;
☐	☐	☐	Electrical inspections of equipment, buildings and services, and portable appliance testing (PAT);
☐	☐	☐	Emergency arrangements – business contingency planning;
☐	☐	☐	Emergency maintenance;
☐	☐	☐	Eye protection;
☐	☐	☐	Fire and emergency (terrorist threat, gas escape, etc.) evacuation arrangements;
☐	☐	☐	First aid arrangements;
☐	☐	☐	Forklift trucks operation;
☐	☐	☐	Safety footwear;
☐	☐	☐	General arrangements for health and safety welfare;
☐	☐	☐	Head protection;

- ❏ ❏ ❏ Hearing protection;
- ❏ ❏ ❏ Hot work – welding, brazing, soldering, flame cutting (hot work permit to work);
- ❏ ❏ ❏ Scaffolds, scaffold towers ladders and steps (working at height);
- ❏ ❏ ❏ Lasers – personal exposure, fire hazard;
- ❏ ❏ ❏ Lifting equipment (lifts, cranes, hoists);
- ❏ ❏ ❏ Lone worker arrangements;
- ❏ ❏ ❏ Machinery selection and operation;
- ❏ ❏ ❏ Manual handling;
- ❏ ❏ ❏ Medical facilities (first aid, health surveillance);
- ❏ ❏ ❏ Noise (occupational and environmental);
- ❏ ❏ ❏ Permit to work procedures (for example, lock-off procedures for maintenance, hot work);
- ❏ ❏ ❏ Personal protective equipment (PPE);
- ❏ ❏ ❏ Planned inspections (safety tours and surveys);
- ❏ ❏ ❏ Planned preventative maintenance;
- ❏ ❏ ❏ Provision of OH&S safeguards in procurement procedures;
- ❏ ❏ ❏ Radiography;
- ❏ ❏ ❏ Respiratory protection;
- ❏ ❏ ❏ Risk assessments;
- ❏ ❏ ❏ Safety policy;
- ❏ ❏ ❏ Safety training – competence;
- ❏ ❏ ❏ Safety training – induction (awareness);
- ❏ ❏ ❏ Safety training – specific for PPE, emergencies, etc;
- ❏ ❏ ❏ Security;
- ❏ ❏ ❏ Skin protection – gloves, overalls, sun cream, etc.;
- ❏ ❏ ❏ Storage;
- ❏ ❏ ❏ Toolbox talks;
- ❏ ❏ ❏ Traffic control/routes;
- ❏ ❏ ❏ Chemical and hazardous substance management for employees;
- ❏ ❏ ❏ Ventilation and extraction systems.

In practice – Existing information, guidance and instructions within the organization

 ### *F&L – office*

While offices are generally low-risk areas, F&L still needs to address all aspects of OH&S within its environment.

Aspects that should already be covered are:

- incident and near miss reporting and investigation;
- COSHH (Control of Substances Hazardous to Health) assessments;
- display screen equipment risk assessments;
- fire and emergency management and evacuation procedures;
- first aid procedures;
- manual handling arrangements;
- health and safety policy;
- safety tours and inspections;
- workplace risk assessments (see The Management of Health & Safety at Work Regulations 1999);
- workplace assessment (see The Workplace (Health, Safety and Welfare) Regulations 1992).

Other safety aspects that may already exist and should be considered are:

- communication of OH&S information – contractors, neighbours;
- induction training procedure;
- task training;
- lone working arrangements;
- planned electrical inspections;
- visitor procedures;
- driving and travelling.

⚙ UE – engineering workshop

Engineering operations, by their very nature, tend to present a wider range of hazards and much higher risks. The level of control required is greater and closer attention needs to be given to the training of employees.

Safety aspects that should already be covered are:

- accident, incident, near miss and occupational ill-health reporting and investigation;
- communication of OH&S information;
- fire and emergency evacuation procedures;
- first aid procedures;
- hot work;
- induction training procedure;
- lifting equipment;
- manual handling arrangements;
- medical facilities;
- noise assessment;
- personal protective equipment – selection and use;
- planned preventative maintenance;
- emergency maintenance – OH&S procedures;
- process training procedures;
- safety targets and objectives;
- safety tours and inspections;
- safety signs and notices;
- working at height;
- workplace risk assessments.

Other safety aspects that may already exist and should be considered are:

- alcohol and substance misuse;
- contractor and visitor management procedures;
- COSHH assessments;
- display screen equipment risk assessments;

- first aid;
- ladder maintenance;
- lone working arrangements;
- machinery purchase (The Provision and Use of Work Equipment Regulations 1998);
- manual handling;
- noise assessment;
- personal protective equipment;
- scaffold controls;
- traffic control/routes;
- other workplace regulation compliance.

LCD – retail

As an operation involving totally different types of activities, LCD needs to ensure it addresses safety aspects in each part of the business. While the retail environment tends to be low risk, the interface with the public does add a dimension that needs to be carefully considered, particularly in view of the unpredictable nature of some members of the public whilst in the store.

Safety aspects that should already be covered are:

- accident and incident reporting and investigation;
- contractors and visitors procedures;
- fire and emergency procedures;
- first aid procedures;
- food hygiene;
- safety signs and notices;
- induction training procedures;
- manual handling arrangements;
- preventative maintenance;
- process training procedure;
- safety targets and objectives;
- safety tours and inspections;

- security arrangements;
- traffic control/routes;
- workplace regulation compliance.

Other safety aspects that may already exist and should be considered are:

- COSHH assessments;
- display screen equipment risk assessments;
- use of ladders and working at height;
- medical facilities (staff and customers);
- personal protective equipment;
- risk assessments (repetitive strain injury issues at checkout facilities);
- storage management.

▰▰▰ B&C – construction

As a company operating in a recognized hazardous environment, B&C needs to promote a strong safety culture both among its own staff and among the subcontractors it employs. As with LCD, the interface with the public also needs to be considered.

Safety aspects that should already be covered are:

- accident, incident and ill health reporting and investigation;
- battery charging;
- compressed air use;
- confined spaces;
- contractor and visitor procedures;
- emergency arrangements;
- first aid;
- forklift trucks;
- hot work;
- induction training;
- lifting equipment;

- manual handling;
- noise;
- personal protective equipment;
- recruit to work procedures – competency assessments;
- risk assessments;
- scaffolds;
- steps and ladders;
- safety targets and objectives;
- safety tours and inspections;
- toolbox talks;
- traffic control/routes.

Other safety aspects that may exist and should be considered are:

- communicating information;
- contractor deliveries;
- COSHH assessments;
- display screen equipment assessments in offices;
- eye protection;
- fire precautions on sites;
- planned inspections;
- security;
- storage arrangements;
- working in hot, cold and wet environments.

 YYIMT.com – new technology

By planning in advance, YYIMT was able to benefit from the experience and information available from other organizations that had learnt by trial and error or from expensive mistakes. Its approach was very systematic, looking at what elements made up the company and how they worked together, thus enabling it to identify the interfaces where information would be required.

Safety aspects that should be covered by documentation are:

- OH&S audits;
- communicating information;
- consultations with employees;
- managing contractors and visitors;
- display screen equipment;
- electrical inspections;
- fire and emergency arrangements;
- first aid;
- general arrangements for health and safety;
- manual handling;
- OH&S safeguards in procurement;
- risk assessment;
- safety targets and objectives;
- safety tours and inspections;
- security;
- storage.

H&H – road haulage

The activities of H&H are based in two areas of delivery: at the business base and during road delivery activities. Business-based activity predominantly consists of office work and vehicle marshalling and storage. Road deliveries need to take account of client workplace interfaces and road safety.

Safety aspects that should already be covered are:

- accident, incident and occupational ill health reporting and investigation;
- contractor and visitor procedures;
- driving;
- fire and emergency procedures;
- first aid procedures;

- food hygiene;
- safety signs and notices;
- induction training procedures;
- manual handling arrangements;
- preventative maintenance;
- process training procedure;
- safety targets and objectives;
- safety tours and inspections;
- security arrangements;
- stress management;
- traffic control/routes;
- workplace regulation compliance.

Other safety aspects that may exist and should be considered are:

- COSHH assessments;
- display screen equipment risk assessments;
- personal protective equipment;
- storage management and safe working loads in warehouse areas;
- security.

Stage 3 – Identify management system arrangements – reference against BS OHSAS 18001

The BS OHSAS 18001 OH&S management model is based on providing and satisfying key criteria for the organization against the following elements:

- policy;
- planning;
- implementation and operation;
- checking and corrective action;
- management review.

This aspect of OH&S management involves examining what the organization already has in place and the success of the existing systems in managing OH&S. It requires a complete and open appraisal of the organization's current controls and procedures.

To help identify what resources are currently being devoted to OH&S management and how these are being applied, the following key questions address your current system and performance. This will be extremely relevant to those with existing BS EN ISO 9001 and/or BS EN ISO 14001 systems. Those without such systems in place need to reference the appropriate chapters and the checklists within them before assigning their implementation status. The self-assessment questionnaire in Appendix 2 is more detailed.

BS OHSAS element	Yes	Partial	No
Policy			
Does your organization define and document its OH&S policy?			
Planning			
Has your organization carried out a thorough identification of all foreseeable hazards associated with its activities?			
Does your organization carry out risk assessments?			
Does the organization implement controls on a hierarchal basis with PPE as the last resort?			
Does your organization identify all legal and other requirements which apply to it?			
Has a top management representative been appointed at the most senior level of the organization and are those with management functions aware of their role, responsibilities and accountability?			

BS OHSAS element	Yes	Partial	No
Implementation and operation			
Does your organization set objectives to ensure continual improvement of OH&S performance?			
Does the organization ensure that those working for or on behalf of the organization are competent for the work they undertake?			
Does your organization carry out training to increase the awareness and knowledge of employees about OH&S issues?			
Do you encourage worker participation in determining the risks and control measures and identifying opportunities for improvement?			
Does your organization provide information about OH&S matters to employees?			
Does your organization provide information about OH&S matters to relevant interested parties, i.e. other than employees?			
Does your organization have a system for gathering relevant OH&S information?			
Does your organization embrace OH&S issues in its operational control system?			
Does your organization have procedures for responding to emergency situations which might endanger OH&S?			
Checking			
Does the organization commit to measuring performance and monitoring?			
Does your organization carry out OH&S audits and act on their findings?			

BS OHSAS element	Yes	Partial	No
Management review			
Does your organization carry out management reviews of its OH&S activities as part of the drive for continual OH&S improvement?			

For those who have more developed systems the following questions will help the organization establish its current implementation status. References to the appropriate requirement in BS OHSAS 18001 are also included.

Yes No

☐ ☐ Do you carry out risk assessment on all your activities? (4.3.1)

☐ ☐ Are your controls and procedures appropriate to the risks involved? (4.3.1)

☐ ☐ Do the control procedures primarily remove the risk? (4.3.1)

☐ ☐ Do you produce an annual OH&S plan with achievable objectives and targets? (4.3.3)

☐ ☐ Are OH&S objectives regularly set and reviewed? (4.3.3)

☐ ☐ Do all your staff actively participate in the OH&S management programme? (4.4.3.2)

☐ ☐ Do your controls and procedures need to be improved? (4.4.6)

☐ ☐ Do you carry out OH&S inspections/tours? (4.5.1)

☐ ☐ Are your OH&S objectives being achieved and showing demonstrable improvement in OH&S performance? (4.5.1)

☐ ☐ Do you regularly review your health and safety management system? (4.6)

☐ ☐ Do you consider your controls and procedures to be cost-effective? (4.6)

☐ ☐ Do your OH&S objectives need redefining? (4.6)

Just throwing resources at OH&S issues to merely comply with legal requirements does not guarantee success. An organization may be devoting a lot of effort to OH&S management for a very poor return. For instance, large organizations can fall into the trap of over-communicating irrelevant information to staff when attempting to discharge their obligations. In practice this is more likely to overwhelm staff, be time-consuming, costly and, more importantly, largely ineffective.

Establishing and maintaining an OH&S management system requires a commitment of time, effort and resources by the organization. In the early stages, the additional responsibility of training may cause disruption to the normal schedule of the organization and business delivery. Moreover, performance can also be disheartening as improvements do not always meet expectations. Indeed, it is not unusual to see an initial surge in incident statistics as staff respond to the new regime and the importance of reporting all incidents. A longer-term view is necessary.

After the introductory phase, an ongoing system to monitor and review the performance of the system is essential to identify where adjustments are required or where the system can beneficially be extended into other parts of the working environment.

To help identify what resources are currently being devoted to OH&S management and how these are being applied, the following checklists ask some key questions about the organization's current performance.

CHECKLIST: Some key questions about the organization's current system

Yes	No	
❏	❏	Are you achieving the objectives set in your annual OH&S plan?
❏	❏	Do you think you are using resources to the best effect?
❏	❏	Do your incident statistics show a continual improvement through a maintained reduction?
❏	❏	Are there noticeable improvements following the findings of safety inspections?
❏	❏	Most importantly, is your management system contributing to your overall business performance, i.e. are the costs of managing OH&S less than your losses would otherwise be through accidents/incidents?

The self-assessment questionnaire in Appendix 2 provides a more in-depth analysis of the status of OH&S within the organization. It can be used as an independent assessment or together with the checklists given previously. The questions are similar to those given in the previous checklist but there are some additional requirements as well.

In practice – Existing resources already devoted to health and safety management

 ### *F&L – office*

F&L's office-based activities provide a relatively low-risk environment. The absence of an adequate incident reporting and investigation procedure, however, disguised two major safety issues: firstly, the large numbers of slip, trip and fall incidents that were occurring; secondly, a significant number of road accidents involving key staff who had to work continuous long hours to cope with business pressures.

 ### *UE – engineering workshop*

All accidents and near-miss incidents are continuously monitored in the engineering environment. This information needs to be cascaded to all staff to enable them to recognize similar situations and take remedial action before an incident occurs. This can be achieved by including safety on the agenda of all management meetings and regular but focused toolbox talks by unit organizers.

The use of staff suggestion schemes can identify savings as well as areas where improved safety management can be achieved.

 ### *LCD – retail*

In a retail environment, customers need to be protected from harmful situations whilst in the store. In addition, where food handling is involved, effective staff training and good housekeeping are of paramount importance.

Adequate OH&S procedures should also cover the interface with the large number of non-LCD personnel, such as those making deliveries. Behind the front line of the business, identical system monitors will apply as in any other organization.

B&C – construction

The very nature of the construction industry makes managing OH&S particularly difficult. This stems from the fact that the industry has a particularly mobile workforce between contracts. To ensure that the organization's procedures were compliant, B&C reviewed and revised its contractor and staff training programme to cover all personnel who worked for B&C. Furthermore, to ensure this information was being used B&C introduced an internal reassessment procedure to monitor understanding and provide refresher training where necessary.

YYIMT.com – new technology

YYIMT's approach was to delegate responsibility for managing OH&S resources through the management structure. This entailed providing strategic OH&S training for all managers and giving incentives to employees to provide positive contributions to improve OH&S performance.

H&H – road haulage

H&H had two distinct areas of business management to control and address. These were based on site operations and activities and also on transport operations. Competency assessment, i.e. driving skills and knowledge, were a fundamental requirement for the driving workforce. Training was used to ensure this policy was enforced and regular reviews of health and safety aspects of contract delivery were carried out to improve performance. A further area of improvement addressed the understanding of driving outside the UK and the application of advanced driver training.

Stage 4A – Determine applicable legal and other requirements

This stage relates to the regulatory control obligations placed on the organization and any other guidance on what is considered good practice. It is very difficult to work through all the regulations etc. that exist. It is recommended that organizations focus on those legal and other requirements that relate to its identified risks, taking into consideration their:

- industry sector;
- activities;
- products, processes, facilities, equipment, materials, personnel;
- business location.

All organizations with five or more employees are required to have a written health and safety statement covering the general arrangements for occupational health and safety. This is the primary source document and should be supported by a series of documented procedures that ensure its correct interpretation and application throughout the organization.

Documentation covering OH&S can be in the form of either:

- guidance summarizing regulatory requirements that apply to the organization; or
- specific instructions covering the safe operation of plant, activities or operations carried out within the organization.

It is not sufficient for an organization to say that it complies with guidance and legislation without being able to provide evidence of direct implementation within the organization.

Sometimes it is clearly understood from the business activity of the organization which guidance and legislation applies, e.g. The Control of Noise at

Work Regulations 2005 will most likely apply in a workshop where there is noise from operating machinery. Other regulatory control may be considered less applicable to the organization, e.g. The Control of Asbestos Regulations 2006, as the organization might consider that it does not work with asbestos even though the material is present in the fabric structure of its buildings. Under these regulations, the organization does in fact have a responsibility – as the duty holder – to ensure that the location and condition of the asbestos is known, together with information on whether it can be disturbed and whether appropriate controls are exercised.

The key legislation and basis for modern occupational health and safety law in the UK is The Health and Safety at Work etc. Act 1974. The Act has produced a whole series of modern regulations covering all parts of industry and commerce. Since 1992, HASWA has been reinforced with the core principles of risk assessment described in the various enactments of the Management of Health and Safety at Work Regulations emanating from EU directives and guidance. From these basic guidelines, risk assessment is now the fundamental element of all successful health and safety management systems.

It is important, however, not to forget that some (albeit diminishing) pre-HASWA legislation may still apply because it has yet to be repealed or revised to meet modern requirements.

Appendix 3 provides guidance on how to obtain information on what legislation, regulation and codes of practice exist that might apply to the organization. The checklist given in this chapter will also help most organizations identify regulations or guidance that relates to their activities. It is important when referring to any piece of legislation or guidance that the user confirms that what they are using is current and relevant to their organization before applying it. More information is available from sources such as the HSE, local authorities, trade associations, trade unions, professional bodies and specialist health and safety consultants. See Appendix 3 for more information.

Some legislation is mandatory for all organizations. HASWA states the following:

- 'It shall be the duty of every employer to prepare ... a written statement of his [sic] general policy with respect to health and safety at work of his employees and the organization and arrangements … in force for carrying out the policy' (2.3);

- 'It shall be the duty … to bring the [policy] statement and any revision to the notice of all employees' (2.3);
- 'It shall be the duty of every employee while at work to take reasonable care of himself or any other persons who may be affected by his acts or omissions' (7);
- 'It shall be the duty of any person who designs, manufactures, imports or supplies any article for use at work to ensure, as far as reasonably practicable, that the article is so designed and constructed as to be safe and without risks to health when properly used' (6).

Some organizations may also need to take account of the national legislation of other countries when working overseas. In these instances, if the UK legislation is the more onerous then it should be followed and vice versa.

The checklist that follows details some of the major legislation applicable to many organizations. A tick box has been provided for identifying those that apply to the organization (1), may apply (2), or are irrelevant (3). The legislation has been separated into two categories:

1. core legislation and regulations applicable to all organizations' activities; and
2. more specific legal responsibilities which may or may not apply, either continually or as a result of the organization's activities.

CHECKLIST: Legislation and regulations that may apply to the organization

			Core legislation and regulations applying to all organizations
1	2	3	
❏	❏	❏	The Health and Safety (Consultation with Employees) Regulations 1996;
❏	❏	❏	Control of Asbestos Regulations 2006;
❏	❏	❏	The Control of Substances Hazardous to Health Regulations 2002 (COSHH);
❏	❏	❏	Corporate Manslaughter and Corporate Homicide Act 2007;
❏	❏	❏	The Health and Safety (Display Screen Equipment) Regulations 1992 (DSE);
❏	❏	❏	The Electricity at Work Regulations 1989;

☐ ☐ ☐ The Fire Precautions Act 1971;

☐ ☐ ☐ The Health and Safety (First-Aid) Regulations 1981;

☐ ☐ ☐ The Health and Safety at Work etc. Act 1974;

☐ ☐ ☐ BS 7671, Requirements for electrical installations — IEE Wiring Regulations;

☐ ☐ ☐ The Management of Health and Safety at Work Regulations 1999 (MHASAW);

☐ ☐ ☐ The Regulatory Reform (Fire Safety) Order 2005;

☐ ☐ ☐ The Reporting of Injuries, Diseases and Dangerous Occurrences Regulations 1995 (RIDDOR);

☐ ☐ ☐ The Safety Representatives and Safety Committee Regulations 1977;

☐ ☐ ☐ The Health and Safety (Safety Signs and Signals) Regulations 1996;

☐ ☐ ☐ The Workplace (Health, Safety and Welfare) Regulations 1992.

Some of the more specific legislation which may or may not apply

☐ ☐ ☐ The Chemicals (Hazard Information and Packaging for Supply) Regulations 1994;

☐ ☐ ☐ The Control of Noise at Work Regulations 2005;

☐ ☐ ☐ The Control of Pollution (Special Waste) Regulations 1980;

☐ ☐ ☐ The Construction (Design and Management) Regulations 2007 (CDM);

☐ ☐ ☐ The Food Safety (General Food Hygiene) Regulations 1995;

☐ ☐ ☐ The Highly Flammable Liquids and Liquefied Petroleum Gases Regulations 1972;

☐ ☐ ☐ The Ionising Radiations Regulations 1999;

☐ ☐ ☐ The Lifting Operations and Lifting Equipment Regulations 1998 (LOLER);

☐ ☐ ☐ The Manual Handling Operations Regulations 1992;

☐ ☐ ☐ The Personal Protective Equipment at Work Regulations 1992;

☐ ☐ ☐ The Pressure Systems and Transportable Gas Containers Regulations 1989;

☐ ☐ ☐ The Provision and Use of Work Equipment Regulations 1998 (PUWER II).

In practice – Application of primary legislation and regulations

While all working environments are subject to core health and safety legislation, for example HASWA, different environments will be subject to duties and responsibilities under more specific regulatory controls. All these environments may be different but they are all linked by a common theme – the existence of hazards, the risks associated with the activities being carried out and the use of control measures to mitigate them. The case studies identify the main risk areas that need to be addressed in the very different environments in which each organization operates. Most of the individual case studies have been broken down into core requirements and requirements that are business-specific. Core requirements will apply to most organizations; business-specific ones have been used in the case studies to assist the reader to determine the risks they themselves may have to address. Chapter 6 provides more specific guidance on risk assessment.

Ideally, the organization should identify its significant risks, as described in Chapter 6, before doing this exercise.

 ## F&L – office

Legislation applying to all F&L activities:

- The Health and Safety (Consultation with Employees) Regulations 1996;
- The Control of Asbestos Regulations 2006;
- The Disability Discrimination Act 1995 (DDA);
- The Health and Safety (Display Screen Equipment) Regulations 1992 (DSE);
- The Electricity at Work Regulations 1989;
- The Health and Safety (First-Aid) Regulations 1981;
- The Health and Safety at Work etc. Act 1974;
- The Management of Health and Safety at Work Regulations 1999;
- The Manual Handling Operations Regulations 1992;
- The Reporting of Injuries, Diseases and Dangerous Occurrences Regulations 1995 (RIDDOR);
- The Health and Safety (Safety Signs and Signals) Regulations 1996;
- The Regulatory Reform (Fire Safety) Order 2005;
- The Workplace (Health, Safety and Welfare) Regulations 1992.

UE – engineering workshop

Legislation applying:

- The Control of Asbestos Regulations 2006;
- The Control of Noise at Work Regulations 2005;
- The Control of Substances Hazardous to Health Regulations 2002 (COSHH);
- The Health and Safety (Display Screen Equipment) Regulations 1992 (DSE);
- The Electricity at Work Regulations 1989;
- The Fire Precautions Act 1971;
- The Health and Safety (First-Aid) Regulations 1981;
- The Food Safety (General Food Hygiene) Regulations 1995;*
- The Health and Safety (Safety Signs and Signals) Regulations 1996;
- The Health and Safety at Work etc. Act 1974;
- The Highly Flammable Liquids and Liquefied Petroleum Gases Regulations 1972;**
- The Lifting Operations and Lifting Equipment Regulations 1998 (LOLER);
- The Management of Health and Safety at Work Regulations 1999;
- The Manual Handling Operations Regulations 1992;
- The Personal Protective Equipment at Work Regulations 1992;
- The Regulatory Reform (Fire Safety) Order 2005;
- The Reporting of Injuries, Diseases and Dangerous Occurrences Regulations 1995 (RIDDOR);
- The Safety Representatives and Safety Committee Regulations 1977;
- The Workplace (Health, Safety and Welfare) Regulations 1992.

* UE has its own canteen.
** UE uses solvents for cleaning and painting.

 *LCD – retail*

Legislation applying:

- The Health and Safety (Display Screen Equipment) Regulations 1992 (DSE);
- The Electricity at Work Regulations 1989;
- The Fire Precautions Act 1971;
- The Health and Safety (First-Aid) Regulations 1981;
- The Food Safety (General Food Hygiene) Regulations 1995;
- The Health and Safety at Work etc. Act 1974;
- The Management of Health and Safety at Work Regulations 1999 (MHASAW);
- The Manual Handling Operations Regulations 1992;
- The Regulatory Reform (Fire Safety) Order 2005;
- The Reporting of Injuries, Diseases and Dangerous Occurrences Regulations 1995 (RIDDOR);
- The Health and Safety (Safety Signs and Signals) Regulations 1996;
- The Workplace (Health, Safety and Welfare) Regulations 1992.

B&C – construction

Legislation applying:

- The Construction (Design and Management) Regulations 2007 (CDM);
- The Health and Safety (Consultation with Employees) Regulations 1996;
- The Control of Asbestos Regulations 2006;
- The Control of Noise at Work Regulations 2005;
- The Control of Pollution (Special Waste) Regulations 1980;
- The Control of Substances Hazardous to Health Regulations 2002 (COSHH);
- The Health and Safety (Display Screen Equipment) Regulations 1992 (DSE);

- The Electricity at Work Regulations 1989;
- The Fire Precautions Act 1971;
- The Health and Safety (First-Aid) Regulations 1981;
- The Health and Safety at Work etc. Act 1974;
- The Highly Flammable Liquids and Liquefied Petroleum Gases Regulations 1972;
- BS 7671, IEE Wiring Regulations;
- The Management of Health and Safety at Work Regulations 1999 (MHASAW);
- The Manual Handling Operations Regulations 1992;
- The Personal Protective Equipment at Work Regulations 1992;
- The Provision and Use of Work Equipment Regulations 1998 (PUWER II);
- The Regulatory Reform (Fire Safety) Order 2005;
- The Reporting of Injuries, Diseases and Dangerous Occurrences Regulations 1995 (RIDDOR);
- The Health and Safety (Safety Signs and Signals) Regulations 1996;
- The Workplace (Health, Safety and Welfare) Regulations 1992;
- The Work at Height Regulations 2005.

 ## YYIMT.com – new technology

Legislation applying:

- The Health and Safety (Consultation with Employees) Regulations 1996;
- The Health and Safety (Display Screen Equipment) Regulations 1992 (DSE);
- The Fire Precautions (Workplace) Regulations 1997;
- The Health and Safety (First-Aid) Regulations 1981;
- The Food Safety (General Food Hygiene) Regulations 1995;
- The Health and Safety at Work etc. Act 1974 (HASWA);
- The Health and Safety (Safety Signs and Signals) Regulations 1996;
- The Control of Substances Hazardous to Health Regulations 2002 (COSHH);
- The Electricity at Work Regulations 1989;

- The Management of Health and Safety at Work Regulations 1999 (MHASAW);
- The Manual Handling Operations Regulations 1992;
- The Regulatory Reform (Fire Safety) Order 2005;
- The Workplace (Health, Safety and Welfare) Regulations 1992.

H&H – road haulage

Legislation applying:

- The Construction (Design and Management) Regulations 2007 (CDM);
- Corporate Manslaughter and Corporate Homicide Act 2007;
- The Electricity at Work Regulations 1989;
- The Fire Precautions Act 1971;
- The Health and Safety (First-Aid) Regulations 1981;
- The Health and Safety at Work, etc. Act 1974 (HASWA);
- The Manual Handling Operations Regulations 1992;
- The Reporting of Injuries, Diseases and Dangerous Occurrences Regulations 1995 (RIDDOR);
- The Health and Safety (Consultation with Employees) Regulations 1996;
- The Control of Asbestos Regulations 2006;
- The Control of Noise at Work Regulations 2005;
- The Control of Pollution (Special Waste) Regulations 1980;
- The Control of Substances Hazardous to Health Regulations 2002 (COSHH);
- The Health and Safety (Display Screen Equipment) Regulations 1992 (DSE);
- The Health and Safety (First-Aid) Regulations 1981;
- The Health and Safety (Safety Signs and Signals) Regulations 1996;
- The Highly Flammable Liquids and Liquefied Petroleum Gases Regulations 1972;
- BS 7671, IEE Wiring Regulations;
- The Management of Health and Safety at Work Regulations 1999 (MHASAW);

- The Personal Protective Equipment at Work Regulations 1992;
- The Provision and Use of Work Equipment Regulations 1998 (PUWER II);
- The Regulatory Reform (Fire Safety) Order 2005;
- The Workplace (Health, Safety and Welfare) Regulations 1992.

Stage 4B – Determine guidance, supplier's information and best practice

This section covers guidance and instruction on occupational health and safety available from organizations and trade associations operating and/or specializing in similar fields of activity.

Very few processes and activities found in organizations are so new that there is no existing information available about them. As the legislation under the HASWA has evolved, so has the amount and type of support necessary to ensure safe working conditions.

Information is readily available from many easily accessible sources, ranging from suppliers who have a legal responsibility to produce guidance on the use of their products, to the HSE and trade associations. Information from the HSE is available in the following forms.

- Approved Codes of Practice (ACOPs) accompanying specific regulations, e.g. The Control of Substances Hazardous to Health Regulations 2002 (COSHH).
- Guidance Notes covering particular subject areas, for example, Medical Series, Plant and Machinery.
- General information, e.g. free leaflets, on areas that are being specifically targeted (often provided free of charge for single copies).
- General health and safety material, e.g. *Essentials of Health and Safety at Work* [10], and specialist electronic software, designed to assist small and medium-sized enterprises (SMEs) raise OH&S awareness.
- Contract research reports.

Trade associations or similar bodies exist to support and co-ordinate technical developments within specific business sectors. Many produce advice and guidance focused on their particular sector. This information is especially valuable as it is invariably based on the real-life experience of other member organizations. Frequently, regulatory bodies such as the HSE endorse this type of guidance.

Similar information can arise out of a consensus between several different operators seeking to set standards within a particular sphere of activity.

Local business safety groups, supported by the Royal Society for the Prevention of Accidents (RoSPA), disseminate information and practical experience among different organizations. This may be the simple sharing of views by professional practising safety managers or specific presentations from invited speakers on specialist topics. Invited speakers may include the HSE, an Environmental Health Officer (EHO) from the local authority, manufacturers of personal protective equipment, or specialist consultants operating in a particular field of activity.

With the development of the Internet, access and search capabilities for information have developed extensively, providing nearly all organizations with quick and ready access to current information both in their home country and overseas.

The following checklist shows possible sources of outside information. Tick boxes are provided for identifying those that are relevant (1), may apply (2), or are irrelevant (3).

CHECKLIST: Sources of information for your organization

1	2	3	HSE
☐	☐	☐	Approved Codes of Practice;
☐	☐	☐	Contract Research Reports;
☐	☐	☐	Employment Medical Advisory Service (EMAS);
☐	☐	☐	Guidance Note Series;
☐	☐	☐	General information, e.g. free leaflets;
☐	☐	☐	Electronic software packages.

Local authority

☐ ☐ ☐ Environmental health officer;
☐ ☐ ☐ Trading standards officer;
☐ ☐ ☐ Medical/health advisers;
☐ ☐ ☐ Business safety groups;
☐ ☐ ☐ Chambers of commerce.

Suppliers

☐ ☐ ☐ Equipment;
☐ ☐ ☐ Materials;
☐ ☐ ☐ Services;
☐ ☐ ☐ Landlords.

Other sources of information

☐ ☐ ☐ British Standards Institution;
☐ ☐ ☐ Business development organizations;
☐ ☐ ☐ Customers;
☐ ☐ ☐ Neighbours;
☐ ☐ ☐ Fire authorities;
☐ ☐ ☐ Insurer/insurance brokers;
☐ ☐ ☐ Trade associations or similar organizations;
☐ ☐ ☐ Other specialist organizations – RoSPA, Institute of Occupational Safety and Health (IOSH), etc;
☐ ☐ ☐ Police (welfare and security);
☐ ☐ ☐ IT providers.

In practice – Best practice and guidance in the particular industry sector

UE – engineering workshop

UE's engineering workshop environment best demonstrates the usefulness of outside sources for information on best practice and guidance. The engineering sector is particularly well served by the HSE, with supporting bodies and specialist organizations providing additional advice:

- *Code of Safe Practice: Application of Powder Coatings by Electrostatic Spraying* [11] (issued by The British Coatings Federation);
- INDG261(rev1), *Pressure systems – safety and you* [12] (HSE);
- HSG231, *Working safely with metalworking fluids* [13] (HSE);
- PM56, *Noise from Pneumatic Systems* [14] (HSE);
- INDG163(rev2), *Five steps to risk assessment* [15] (HSE);
- HSG202, *General ventilation in the workplace* [16] (HSE).

Stage 5 – Determine gaps between what is in place and what the organization needs to manage

Having completed the processes of identifying hazards and quantifying risks, current arrangements in place etc. the next stage is to determine what gaps have to be filled.

The implementation plan can be based on the approach given in Chapter 5 with respect to objectives and programmes. In doing so the following points should be taken into consideration.

- Fundamental to all successful OH&S management is the principle of effective risk assessment. This applies to all aspects of business activity and should ensure that mitigation in one area does not increase the risk burden in another – either within the business or outside, e.g. for contractors or neighbours. Similar guidelines are found in OHSAS 18002, although here the emphasis is to establish the principles for hazard identification, risk assessment and control – across normal, abnormal and potential emergency operational conditions.
- Very few organizations are so unique that they have no peers. Consequently, areas of best operational health and safety practice should be identified from any source, within or outside the UK.
- Although organizations can be similar in their management delivery, they are rarely the same and, as such, all guidance and best practice adopted for the organization will need to be tailored to its particular needs before

it is implemented. Implementation can only be achieved when it is communicated, trained and briefed to those who need it.

- Often what employees perceive as the only solution is adapted successfully by them to work in a more effective way. This can extend across the whole of the organization, e.g. the sales executive who closes the deal with a client recognizing that there are constraints on delivery of the finished product.

- Both the health and safety aspects of management should be taken into account. Safety in relation to accident prevention is often well regulated and guidelines clearly developed, e.g. working at height, whereas other work-related physical and mental health issues can often be missed, particularly when they are chronic in nature, e.g. asbestosis, which can take many years to develop.

- Mitigation should follow the established principles of elimination, replacement, individuals, control (engineering), personal protective equipment, discipline (ERICPD).

- All organizations have to be compliant with most of the HASWA and other general statutory provision, e.g. The Management of Health and Safety at Work Regulations 1999 (MHASAW). More specific legislation such as The Health and Safety (Display Screen Equipment) Regulations 1992 (DSE) will also apply to those organizations functioning with conventional business techniques. In specialized areas, organizations will have more specific statutory provisions to meet, such as those governing food safety hygiene.

- The ISR will determine how best to measure OH&S management effectiveness. Many areas will respond to conventional audit and inspection techniques – these will be identified together with the need for more specialist tools.

- As with all aspects of business performance, review processes should exist to monitor management system effectiveness and identify what subsequent targets are established to lead to continual improvement.

3

Defining an OH&S policy

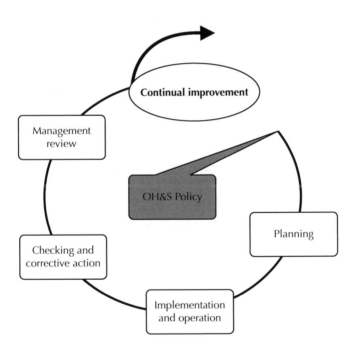

In brief

The OH&S policy is a written statement demonstrating the commitment of an organization to OH&S. It is a formal declaration by top management committing them to implementing a system for preventing harm to those who may be affected by their activities. Ideally it should be less than a page in length, written in simple language and dated and signed by the CEO or appropriate director with responsibility at board level for health and safety.

Defining an OH&S policy

Every organization must be committed to protecting the safety and health of its employees and all others that might be affected by its work activities.

BS OHSAS 18001, 4.2 requires top management to: 'define and authorize the organization's OH&S policy'.

The OH&S policy demonstrates the commitment of an organization by establishing an overall sense of direction and by setting the principles that underpin the actions to be taken. It is a formal commitment by the organization's top management to deliver the necessary financial and human resources for effective OH&S management. The involvement of the top management in producing, authorizing, communicating and promoting the OH&S policy is therefore essential.

There is a legal obligation on every organization in the UK with five or more employees to prepare a written statement of general policy on occupational health and safety and similar requirements exist in many other countries. Most organizations should therefore already have a mission statement committing themselves to managing health and safety effectively. This alone, however, is insufficient to develop a successful OH&S management system. To ensure delivery, the organization needs to support it with more detailed policy statements together with objectives to implement it in practice.

BS OHSAS 18001, ILO-OSH and BS 8800 have established sound guidance for organizations developing an OH&S policy. The following points are based on the requirements specified in BS OHSAS 18001, 4.2, with additional guidance based on ILO-OSH, 3.1 and BS 8800, 3.3, where appropriate.

BS OHSAS 18001 specifies eight key requirements for an OH&S policy.

1. **Appropriate to the nature and scale of the organization's OH&S risks**
   The policy should be realistic, neither overstating the nature of the risks that the organization faces, nor trivializing them. The reader should be capable of appreciating the types of risks and complexity of the organization.

2. **Includes a commitment to prevention of injury and ill health and continual improvement in OH&S management and OH&S performance**
   Inevitably, society's expectations are increasing the pressure on organizations to reduce the risk of ill health, injury, accidents and near-miss incidents in the workplace. It is impossible to make every workplace totally safe but management is expected to commit to preventing injury and ill health. In the case of ill health, this includes stress as well as other disabling effects from exposure to harmful hazards in the workplace environment or from the natural environment, e.g. exposure to avian flu.

   Organizations need to achieve not only a high level of OH&S performance but also to seek a continual improvement in that performance. In addition to meeting legal requirements, the aim should be to move forward, in a cost-effective manner, improving OH&S performance and continuously evolving the OH&S management system to meet changing business and legislative needs. The organization should also take account of the 'lessons learnt' from accident/incident investigations, audit findings and best practice from similar industries or relevant cases taken from the experience of other industries.

3. **Includes a commitment to at least comply with applicable legal requirements and with other requirements to which the organization subscribes that relate to its OH&S hazards**
   'Other requirements' covers voluntary programmes, collective agreements, codes of practice, corporate or group policies, internal standards and specifications. Some legislative requirements cross boundaries with other

disciplines such as environmental management and product design and these issues may also need to be addressed.

4. **Provides the framework for setting and reviewing OH&S objectives**
   Policy statements should enable realistic objectives and management programmes to be established. This demonstrates that the policy is 'not just words' but has real meaning and there is genuine commitment with respect to resources etc. Only a policy that has objectives with tangible outcomes that can be measured and audited can be shown to be working.

5. **Is documented, implemented and maintained**
   The organization's top management should set in place procedures to define, document and endorse its OH&S policy, which should be set out in a succinct policy statement that is signed and dated by the top manager with responsibility for OH&S. Recognizing OH&S as an integral part of improving business performance is the key to successful implementation. Planning and adequate preparation are essential. Often, policy statements and objectives are unrealistic because there are inadequate or inappropriate resources available to deliver them. Before making any public declarations, the organization must ensure that the necessary finance, skills and empowerment are available and that any targets are realistically achievable within this framework.

6. **Is communicated to all persons working under the control of the organization with the intent that they are made aware of their individual OH&S obligations**
   Everyone working on behalf of the organization, whether employees, sub-contractors, agents etc. should be recognized as being equally important.

   The involvement and participation of employees and their representatives is vital in order to gain commitment and to ensure the success of an OH&S management system. Involving employees is often neglected. In most, if not all industries, employees wish to contribute positively to OH&S management to reduce the likelihood of accidents and incidents. They recognize that OH&S needs to be managed cost-effectively to maintain the security of their employment and the quality of their work environment. Engaging employees at this early stage provides them with shared ownership and helps with implementation of OH&S management system arrangements.

Management of OH&S should be a prime responsibility of line management, from the most senior executive to first-line supervisory level. It must never be seen as a specialist function. Including a safety objective as part of the annual management performance review of all managers reinforces this responsibility as well as maintaining an individual focus on the organization's specific safety targets.

Employees at all levels should receive appropriate training to ensure that they are competent to carry out their duties and responsibilities. Training must be appropriate to the needs of each employee and to the benefit of the organization. Training should not be a 'one-off' but should instead be tailored to business demands and supported by appropriate refresher courses to maintain standards and awareness. Initial induction training should be used to demonstrate to new staff from day one the genuine commitment of the organization to effective OH&S management.

In those organizations undertaking project or development work, designers need to be aware not only of present risks but also of possible future risks they may impose if they do not consider safety at the planning and design stage. Current legislation, such as The Construction (Design and Management) Regulations 2007 (CDM), requires occupational health and safety at the earliest design stage. This should be the overriding philosophy in all organizations.

It is a common misconception that the only employees needing training are those working at the sharp end. This is not the case: management and employees at all levels should understand their responsibilities and be competent to undertake the tasks they are required to perform, including managing OH&S.

7. **Is available to interested parties**

The policy statement should be made available to interested parties. The OH&S policy enables the organization to demonstrate to its stakeholders how OH&S management is being developed. The process should ensure that the OH&S policy is available on request but need not necessarily provide for unsolicited copies.

Periodic reporting of OH&S management performance, both internally and externally, to interested parties, provides added benefit.

8. **Is reviewed periodically to ensure that it remains relevant and appropriate to the organization**

The policy should be reviewed periodically to ensure that it remains relevant and appropriate to the organization.

Change is inevitable and, as a driver of continual improvement, top management should ensure the OH&S policy and management system is reviewed regularly in order to meet changing circumstances. This might arise from issues such as new business demands, legislation and technology as well as, most importantly, the lessons learnt from accident/incident investigation, audit findings and best practice.

What is not stated within the requirements of BS OHSAS 18001 is that leadership is of prime importance. The top management needs to lead by example and set the standard. There is no point in setting rules which are not followed by those in the most senior positions. For instance, if an operator is required to wear a high visibility vest in a defined area then managers must also wear one. It is very important to develop a safety culture within the organization which is well embedded. In the absence of such leadership and culture (which are inextricably linked), the fine words of a policy will have little meaning.

The following checklist asks some key questions about the organization's policy and the commitments included in its present policy statement. A tick box is provided for identifying those you have already considered (1) and those you may need to consider (2).

CHECKLIST: The organization's policy statement

1	2	
❏	❏	Is the policy designed to minimize risk and prevent injury, ill health, diseases and incidents?
❏	❏	Does top management demonstrate commitment by example?
❏	❏	Is the policy appropriate to the nature and scale of your organization's risks?
❏	❏	Do you provide adequate and appropriate resources to implement your policy, including competent personnel to deliver the OH&S policy?

❏ ❏ Is OH&S recognized and implemented as an integral part of your business performance?

❏ ❏ Does the policy commit to prevention of harm?

❏ ❏ Do you include commitment, to a high level, of continual cost-effective improvement in your OH&S performance?

❏ ❏ Do you make management of OH&S a prime responsibility of your line managers, from your most senior executive down to your first-line supervisors?

❏ ❏ Does it promote the health and safety of employees?

❏ ❏ Do you know and understand your historical OH&S performance?

❏ ❏ Do you identify your main OH&S hazards?

❏ ❏ Do you include a commitment to comply with currently applicable OH&S legislation and with other requirements to which the organization subscribes?

❏ ❏ Does the policy acknowledge that people are a key resource?

❏ ❏ Do you allow and encourage employee involvement, participation and consultation?

❏ ❏ Do you allow and encourage employee involvement in all aspects of the development and implementation of OH&S policy?

❏ ❏ Are you committed to continual employee training to a level allowing them to carry out their duties competently?

❏ ❏ Do you ensure that everyone working on your behalf is made aware of their individual OH&S obligations?

❏ ❏ Is the policy and performance made readily available to other interested parties?

❏ ❏ Is your policy and management system reviewed periodically to ensure that it remains relevant and appropriate to the organization as part of the drive for continual improvement?

❏ ❏ Do you set and publish OH&S targets and objectives?

4

Creating a climate for effective OH&S management

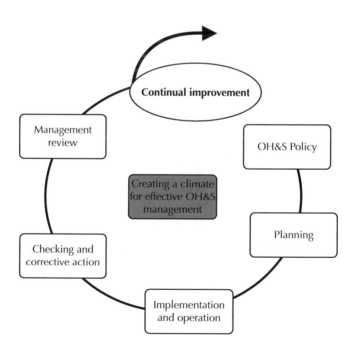

In brief

This chapter is about changing hearts and minds. Creating a positive climate in an organization with respect to occupational health and safety is the fundamental ingredient of effective OH&S management.

It is increasingly evident that developing a positive safety culture is vital when it comes to enabling an organization to achieve excellence in managing occupational health and safety.

Some organizations appear to have effective systems on paper (or electronically) that are highly comprehensive yet in reality there is little commitment to deliver and the output in performance terms is poor.

Building a positive safety culture sustaining a robust system that continually improves can be difficult to achieve. It often takes time to build up the trust and co-operation of the workforce. It is hard to ensure that supervisors/managers do not just subscribe to good practice when it is convenient and then forget everything when they have to meet challenging production targets.

Safety culture is usually inseparable from an organization's overall business ethic and can rarely be managed in isolation. Therefore, many of the characteristics are common. The culture of the organization is very much influenced by the leadership. All too often we see that workers have to wear protective equipment while it seems to be thought unnecessary for managers to wear such equipment while on the shop floor, despite the fact that they would be exposed to the same risks in this situation and should be leading by example. This is unacceptable and there are many such barriers that prevent a positive culture being developed. Examples of positive characteristics are given in Annex C of BS 8800 and the following are based on some of these.

- Staff are committed to the aims of their organization and the way the organization is managed.
- Top management and senior staff demonstrate visible OH&S commitment, including in their personal behaviour, showing leadership by example. They make it clear that they are keen to hear bad news as well as good news and they will take action on the information they receive in a blame-free environment.

- Senior staff and supervisors spend time discussing and promoting OH&S in the work environment; commend safe behaviour and express concern if OH&S procedures are not being followed.
- OH&S is managed with the same determination as other key business objectives.
- OH&S is a normal topic of day-to-day discussion in the workplace and there is active feedback on performance.

Equally there are many factors that can impair the culture, e.g.:

- inconsistencies in rules and procedures;
- supervisors and managers not acting upon non-compliances with OH&S rules, e.g. when there is a production emergency;
- rules and procedures developed without due consideration for their practicability;
- rules and safeguards imposed by external agencies and consultants that do not take into account the complexity of the operation and the challenges of compliance;
- situations that present opportunities for ego enhancement, e.g. public displays of daring;
- failures to communicate shortcomings in OH&S arrangements;
- suggestions for improvements or changes from employees are not welcomed and/or are not acted upon;
- there is no employee involvement in, e.g. preparing risk assessments, developing operating procedures or carrying out accident and incident investigations;
- there is an acceptance that violations are inevitable and that little can be done to eliminate them;
- a culture of personal blame exists;
- underestimation of the magnitude of risk for any reason;
- lack of support for personal problems, leading to impairment of an individual's ability to act safely;
- concentration is placed on statistics when fact-finding and acting on the facts is more important.

There is no quick way to overcome lack of commitment. This has to be gained by promoting good practices such as those given in the initial list above. It is essential to involve the workforce and ask them what needs to be done to enable work to be carried out safely and effectively. The importance of involving the workforce, who know what the real problems are and can provide positive solutions at the same time as ensuring that efficiency is not compromised (or even improving it), cannot be overemphasized. The following is an example of what one large chemical manufacturing company did when it found a lack of commitment to wearing essential personal protective equipment.

Selected employees (on a rota with the full support of their colleagues) were asked to observe and record employees not wearing PPE. The names were not recorded but individuals' reasons for not wearing the required protection was recorded. The survey resulted in the amazing observation that only one size of gloves was available and this resulted in 50 per cent of the workforce not wearing them. The change in attitude resulting from the whole exercise helped promote a far more positive culture towards OH&S issues. This, in turn, reduced the number of avoidable injuries considerably as well as absenteeism from work (a significant cost to the organization).

One way of establishing the present situation in an organization is through the use of attitude surveys or the HSE's *Health and Safety Climate Survey Tool* [17]. A question set is given in BS 8800 but care should be exercised in formulating questions that are relevant to the individual organization rather than just using a standard format.

In practice – Creating a climate for effective OH&S management

In each of the following case studies, there are particular points of reference that specifically helped the organization to progress.

F&L – office

The expansion of F&L into dealing with more high profile international clients made the organization more open to acts of intimidation by external forces, e.g. groups that might disagree with the support F&L provides for its clients. While this wasn't an immediate or obvious threat to the organization, the F&L mail and despatch department were the first to recognize the personal threat they were under as the first line of contact with F&L if an anonymous attack were to be made by using the mail facilities. The management recognized this concern and took immediate action to consider how a threat to health and safety could occur and how it could be controlled by involving the mail room staff in the evaluation process.

The examples they came up with below were simple but not necessarily obvious.

- Physical attack on office individuals via weaker points in the building – the mail department was at the back of the building and not accessed via the controlled reception.
- Mail came in a variety of sizes and forms, hence it was easy to hide an explosive device.
- Opening mail was done as a matter of urgency, hence little attention was paid to being aware of the content, i.e. whether there were explosive devices or even dangerous chemical contents.
- No one in the department would be aware if a higher than normal threat level existed.
- The department had no instruction or means of dealing with a suspect package.

As part of the employee–management consultation process, senior management discussed with the department what the potential threats could be and what risks there were to personnel, the company and the structure of the office. This led to the following changes being made.

- All clients that F&L took on would be reviewed against the threat level they posed. This would be reviewed at various critical stages of involvement and the information gained used to alert the mail department to be particularly sensitive to mail for the F&L personnel involved, or where mail originated from certain countries. The office arranged to use a coloured threat level against higher risk cases so that all staff were readily aware of the risk.
- CCTV was installed to increase security surveillance around the mail room.
- Mail would be screened for suspect conditions, e.g. feeling for wires or soft pliable contents that may indicate a chemical substance.
- Opening of packages would be more carefully done.
- Staff were involved in drawing up instructions for how to open suspect mail, what should be done if a higher risk was suspected and how an emergency would be managed.

As a final point, these conditions and arrangements were tested with a dummy package, the exercise proving that the conditions had improved. The action helped create a better overall working climate since the staff felt reassured that F&L had taken their concerns seriously and had involved them in addressing the risks.

UE – engineering workshop

The UE workshop environment was always an active one with working machinery and movements of people and internal transport. While the work tasks were all covered by risk assessments and safe working practices, when looked at as a single big picture the operations of UE could be seen to be moving towards organized chaos, bringing increased risk.

Senior management recognized that any changes that were made had to involve the workforce to prevent interruption to productivity and to ensure their 'buy in' to the control measures adopted. Joint discussions were held that identified the following steps to ensure the risk factor would not increase and to improve the working environment further.

- All operating areas would have the floor painted a specific colour, coded in accordance with the risk that existed and the activity being carried out. Machines were allocated a red floor risk zone which could not be entered when the equipment was operational without the authority of the machine operator. This would improve the operator's concentration levels.
- Waste areas would be clearly defined and segregated and, more importantly, located on a collection route for the staff responsible for removing the material. This was also applied to the finished product collection. Both these initiatives immediately led to an improvement in productivity and a more organized despatch process as the finished products were part prepared at the point of manufacture for despatch.
- A routine out-of-hours floor cleaning process and renewal of the colour zones was implemented. This had the added advantage of creating an environment more visually acceptable to visitors as well as giving staff a feeling of pride and a sense of well-being that UE valued the work they carried out.

LCD – retail

LCD's primary business focus had always been to present a professional, customer-based image. The store front was their window and means of attracting custom. Consequently, the primary effort was expended in this area. While OH&S was always taken seriously and applied across all areas of LCD activity, it was seen as being part of compliance and instruction not as part of the LCD image.

To overcome this situation, LCD consulted with employees on what other improvements could be made to the health and safety image of the store. The one area that was immediately raised was the back of store area which the public did not see. While it was still covered by the health and safety regime that applied throughout the store, the promotion of health and safety was a lower priority than in the public areas where the implications could be greater. This gave the employees the feeling that management were only interested in the customers and the public area.

To address this problem, LCD created two champions, one taking responsibility for the front of the store and one for the back of the store. This recognition of there being two distinct operating zones within LCD enabled the collection and sharing of good practice ideas across the two areas of LCD activity. As a result, changes to operating procedures involving delivery lorry distribution were made to further reduce the manual handling element of the warehouse area of LCD activities.

The creation of a warehouse, storage and delivery health and safety forum increased employee involvement and allowed more focused changes to be implemented for the benefit of common areas.

▓▓▓ B&C – construction

B&C's expansion into overseas construction meant that it had to apply health and safety good practice in the UK to a totally different environment. This entailed complying with the national legislative standards that applied in the relevant country and at the same time ensuring that the contracting interfaces it worked with adopted the same approach to health and safety as B&C did.

This was a major challenge to the supervisory staff and the employees that B&C brought to the construction process. One immediate issue was ensuring that plant and equipment under planned preventative maintenance regimes would always be compliant. While instruction and information would always be given, a clear simple mechanism was needed to provide a message as to the current maintenance status for the site.

This was overcome by taking the colour coded status of equipment to another level by displaying identical coloured wind socks at locations that could be seen all around the site to show what was current for that period. All a user of equipment had to do was ensure that the equipment they were using had an ID colour code that agreed with the colour of the wind sock. The approach of providing a simple piece of information that was not driven by an instruction that had to cross a language divide prompted further improvements in the exchange of health and safety information during B&C's overseas activities.

YYIMT.com – new technology

The YYIMT culture of health and safety management was driven by the use of IT equipment and the major problem was managing the break periods that employees needed away from their workstations to prevent them staying in a sedentary position. Senior management were concerned that if all staff took a break every hour for 5 minutes then lost working time would be considerable.

Following a staff consultation programme, the introduction of more flexible working enabled YYIMT to introduce an alarm tool to workstations that alerted employees to the need to take a maximum 5 minute break away from the workstation. These 5 minutes also counted as part of their normal lunch hour, which was reduced to 30 minutes. This way the employees actually finished work 30 minutes earlier. YYIMT maintained its production and having an extended but flexible working day with employees not all arriving and leaving at the same time enabled YYIMT to service its clients over a longer period of the working day.

H&H – road haulage

H&H's activities took place 24 hours a day, seven days a week to meet its clients' demands. After dark deliveries were always least popular amongst driving crews as delivery had to be made to customer sites where the lighting level was poor and vehicle movements could mean a driver being hit by an unexpected vehicle.

Senior management at H&H had difficulty in understanding the issue, believing that with the use of mandatory high visibility clothing driver crews would always be seen, until a staff meeting reported three near-miss events of this type in a single week. Further consultation revealed that these types of incident were very common but were not collated.

The initial action was to include near-miss reporting as part of the accident reporting process. Employees were provided with a small and simple report book to record their load destination and the vehicle number when a near-miss event occurred. This captured the data but did not help solve the problem until a review of reports with the delivery crew representatives examined what else was needed.

The conclusion they came to was based on the flashing hazard warning indicators which vehicles used. As well as a conventional high visibility vest, driver crews were issued with a flashing light tabard that fitted over the vest. This alerted other drivers to an individual before the reflection of the high visibility clothing was visible.

All of the examples described have a common theme: the interaction between the management and the workforce. These can be brought together to describe four defined stages in creating a positive climate for effective OH&S management.

1. First and foremost is management commitment to dialogue. This is the primary driver without which a safety culture cannot evolve.
2. Out of the dialogue comes management recognition and acceptance that employees at the point of delivery do actually have a clearer understanding of the risks – often more so than the manager.
3. Out of this recognition comes a commitment to co-operate in making changes to health and safety delivery.
4. The final level is the decision to make the change rather than accept that no more can be done or needs to be done.

Continual improvement is achieved by ensuring a consistency of approach and, most importantly, not being complacent. This involves challenging what is being done and asking: how can it be done better?

❑	❑	Designating responsibility, resources and authority for achieving objectives;
❑	❑	Ensuring that there is sufficient knowledge, skills and experience to effectively manage OH&S;
❑	❑	Operational plans for implementing risk controls;
❑	❑	Operational plans for implementing legal and other requirements;
❑	❑	Operational control activities for ensuring that OH&S policy is implemented and effectively managed;
❑	❑	Arrangements for measuring, auditing and reviewing OH&S performance to identify any shortfalls and necessary corrective actions;
❑	❑	Arrangements for implementing corrective actions.

Arrangements

❑	❑	Stated plan objectives;
❑	❑	Provision of employee and financial resources appropriate to the organization;
❑	❑	Emergency and contingency plans for foreseeable events;
❑	❑	Organizational arrangements;
❑	❑	Change management arrangements – replacing key personnel;
❑	❑	Organizational change arrangements – as a result of restructuring;
❑	❑	Interfacing with other parties – regulatory bodies, emergency services, etc.;
❑	❑	Managing work–life balance;
❑	❑	Employee support when returning to work after a work-related adverse event, e.g. accident.

In practice – Planning

BS OHSAS 18001 and OHSAS 18002 do not give practical examples of the planning process. BS 8800, however, provides a case study for planning improved hearing protection as an objective.

In each of the following case studies, there are particular points of reference that specifically helped the organization to progress.

 F&L – office

The allocation of safety management responsibilities to a senior manager who received appropriate training ensured a co-ordinated approach across the whole organization. This was extended to ensure that document control was exercised across all business documentation management systems. F&L was particularly concerned about adequate resources being available at all times, e.g. during leave periods, and cover being recognized and provided for during periods of sickness absence.

Initially it adopted a very simple approach to hazard identification and risk assessment. It asked all employees to identify those issues that were of concern to them and used a two-by-two matrix (see the following table) for the evaluation and prioritization process.

Likelihood of harm	Severity of harm – slight	Severity of harm – extreme
Unlikely	Low risk	Medium risk
Very likely	Medium risk	High risk

This led to categories of low, medium and high risk being assigned.

One of the major concerns identified by employees was the risks faced when travelling, which was of particular importance to them as the organization expanded into working overseas. This was identified as high risk and F&L needed to ensure that effective OH&S management controls were implemented, e.g. security and welfare of travellers, personal security requirements.

UE – engineering workshop

A UE objective was the elimination of forklift truck incidents that had frequently occurred on the site. By introducing an inspection and training regime for operators, UE eliminated those incidents that were previously put down to operator error. Refresher training on a three-monthly basis reinforced the message.

Modern technology places new pressures and stresses on employees. UE recognized that technology-driven stress issues needed to be identified and eliminated, especially for the less computer literate of the workforce.

🛒 LCD – retail

Assigning one of the managers with the responsibility for OH&S and food hygiene safety achieved the desired improvements in a short period of time.

A visitor and reception area was introduced to ensure that all people could be accounted for and visitors were made aware of LCD's safety and emergency management arrangements. Hosts were made aware that they were responsible for their visitors and were required to ensure that the organization knew who was coming when, where they would be and any special arrangements needed for them during their visit. This approach was extended to deliveries, trade visits and contractors maintaining LCD services, especially during abnormal hours.

▰▰ B&C – construction

Major weaknesses recognized within B&C were ensuring the mandatory use of personal protective equipment and that all staff had the necessary level of safety competence. To overcome these, B&C initiated an intensive training programme for site managers, supported by regular performance assessments and refresher training. The aim was to ensure that everyone was confirmed as having the required level of safety competence and that they always used and knew how to maintain the PPE provided.

As the organization expanded, taking advantage of the relaxation of cross-border employment restrictions, competency assessments needed to become multilingual.

YYIMT.com – new technology

To prevent the occurrence of repetitive strain injury YYIMT introduced a programme of exercises for its display screen equipment operatives to carry out during the course of their shifts. In addition, it introduced a medical screening programme to identify persons with existing or potential work-related upper limb disorders, to enable particular attention to be paid to their workstation set up.

H&H – road haulage

H&H recognized that it had certain key posts not just for business delivery but also for the management of OH&S. This was reinforced when the manager responsible for OH&S suddenly went on long-term sick leave and a replacement was urgently required. The absence of someone able to immediately take on the role provided H&H with the spur to review all company positions and establish key post credentials, enabling cover to be trained and standards set to provide replacements when needed.

In detail – Planning

Before starting planning, it is important to recognize that the OH&S management system is likely to be more effective and will contribute to improving overall business performance if:

- there is commitment from the outset at the highest level of the organization and this commitment is reinforced throughout the overall organization;
- it is an integral part of the organization's business management system;
- it is based on a proactive approach. Preventing avoidable accidents, occupational ill health, hazardous situations and other adverse event reports using well-managed control measures supported by training, is far better (and cheaper) than reacting to the aftermath of problems as and when they arise;
- there is commitment to continual improvement of OH&S performance throughout the organization. It is sometimes quite erroneously concluded that the absence of incidents or accidents is evidence of good health

and safety practice. This may not be the case. Such a situation can arise because there is a fear of reporting or there is an absence of reporting procedures and this should not be allowed to lead to complacency;

- there is a flexible approach to cope with changing circumstances. For example, the introduction of new or amended legislation, corporate business developments such as The Combined Code on Corporate Governance and Code of Best Practice, changes in materials or processes, developments in technology, organizational changes, staff turnover, etc.;
- it draws together all the relevant experience available to the organization to determine the best approach. For larger organizations, establishing task teams working in different parts and at different levels in the organization may be appropriate. In any organization, responsibility should not be left with one person only.
- Plans are clearly documented and management system outputs recorded as evidence for audit purposes.

Process for OH&S planning

The process for OH&S planning is no different to that which should be used to plan and implement change in any other aspect of the organization's operations. There are four key stages, as shown in the following diagram (please note that, for completeness, this diagram also covers the implementation and review stages).

Stage 1. Drawing up an initial list of OH&S objectives

This stage answers the question: how does the organization get where it wants to be? Time spent here pays dividends later in ensuring that resources are targeted effectively and that the organization prioritizes its efforts towards those areas where there is the greatest risk.

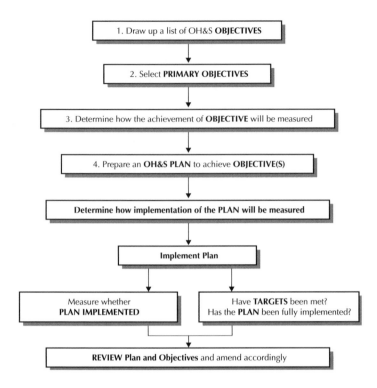

The three major information sources for this stage are the initial status review (see Chapter 2), the risk assessment process (see Chapter 6) and the results of the management review (see Chapter 10).

Other sources of information include:

- regulatory requirements, industry best practice and benchmarking;
- audit reports;
- performance measured against previous OH&S objectives;
- technological options;
- financial, operational and business requirements;
- views of employees and interested parties;
- records of accidents, incidents, near-miss reports, property damage, etc.;
- regulatory body reports.

It is important when gathering information to ensure a broad cover as is necessary to meet the demands of the organization.

The following 'guide words', shown with some examples, are useful in drawing up an initial list of OH&S objectives:

increase/improve – near-miss reporting; machinery safeguards; training; use of personal protective equipment; communications; employees' perception of risks;

maintain/continue – workplace inspections; training; accident and near-miss reporting;

reduce – hazardous conditions; specific hazardous events, e.g. relating to slips, trips and falls; exposure to hazardous substances;

introduce – risk assessment; an emergency plan; a system for active monitoring; strategic OH&S training for senior managers; permit-to-work systems for specified tasks;

eliminate/substitute – all hazardous events; usage of specified hazardous substances; use of damaged and unsuitable equipment;

develop – programmes for administering all aspects of OH&S;

integrate – identify and implement where savings and greater efficiencies can be found, e.g. across OH&S and environmental auditing.

Stage 2. Selecting primary objective

The next stage is to prioritize the objectives from the initial list in order to select the key one(s) that match the OH&S needs of the organization and the resources available.

When selecting objectives, it is important to make sure that they are specific, relevant and achievable in a reasonable period of time.

In developing an OH&S management system, the organization is facilitating a change in its culture towards improving the management of OH&S issues. Involving the workforce by concentrating first on those objectives that can be achieved easily at minimal cost helps build confidence and momentum (provided this is consistent with the prioritizing of risks). As commitment grows, the more difficult issues can be addressed.

Stage 3. Quantifying objectives and selecting performance indicators

The aim should be to set objectives which, if at all possible, are quantifiable and can be measured. The point is that 'what you can't measure, you can't manage'.

The following list shows how the guidewords for objectives, as previously described, might be quantified:

increase/improve – specify a numerical figure and date for achievement;
maintain/continue – specify existing level of activity;
reduce – specify a numerical figure and date for achievement;
introduce – specify a date for achievement;
eliminate or substitute – specify a date for achievement.

In order to determine whether objectives are being achieved, it is good practice to select indicators (guidance on selecting indicators that can be measured is given in Chapter 8).

The objectives finally chosen should be 'SMART':

- **S**pecific
- **M**easurable
- **A**chievable
- **R**ealistic
- **T**ime based.

Stage 4. Preparing plans to achieve objective(s)

The final stage in the planning process answers the question: how does the organization achieve the desired result? The broad content of the plan should be developed by breaking down the key objectives into the individual elements that need to be put in place, such as training, consultation, communication and information-gathering. For each element, the plan should specify the detailed performance targets necessary to implement it: *who* is to do *what*, by *when* and with what *result*. The arrangements need to be such that they can be readily audited by an independent source.

Performance targets can be listed as a series of questions to act as a checklist for those responsible for achieving them. Whatever form is chosen, it should be clearly drafted so that designated persons/teams know exactly what they have to do. Those who are to be allocated targets to achieve should be consulted about their practicality and become competent in undertaking the task(s) assigned to them. The documentation for the targets can later be used to check whether the plan has been implemented.

The resource implications of the plan should also be considered. The financial aspects should be calculated and adequate time and financial resources made available to those assigned the key responsibilities, with periodic reviews undertaken to ensure that the resources are still sufficient and appropriate. The final plan will need to be fully resourced and taken forward with the complete support of senior management to ensure implementation.

BS 8800, 3.5.2 states: 'The key elements to planning and setting the objectives are as follows.

a) 'The organization's objectives should be clearly defined and prioritized.'
    Objectives should clearly relate to individual and specific aspects of the organization's activities. Priorities should be risk-based, i.e. they should address the major risks first rather than just the easy ones.
b) 'Objectives should be specific to the organization and appropriate relative to its size, the nature of its activities, the hazards, risks and the conditions in which it operates.'
    The objectives should be realistic. Often an organization will be overambitious and set unachievable targets over unrealistic timescales, resulting in all parts of the organization becoming disillusioned at the lack of progress.
c) 'Suitable and specific performance indicators should be chosen to measure whether objectives have been or are being achieved.'
    Measurement criteria should be realistic and positive. Negatives will always be apparent and should not be ignored, whereas small positive

gains will always maintain momentum. Consider taking the negatives and turning them into positives, e.g. as a learning exercise.

d) 'Plans should be prepared to achieve each objective.'

An action plan should be devised and revisited regularly to monitor progress. The organization should not be afraid to change its focus when progress has been made, diverting resources to where additional support is required.

e) 'Adequate financial, human resources and technical support should be made available.'

From the outset resource planning is essential. Once objectives are agreed, the commitment to delivery should be as strong as it would be for meeting a customer's order or requirements or any other business demand.

Some organizations set up the OH&S management process as another 'customer' to ensure commitment is focused.

f) 'The full implementation of plans should be measured.'

g) 'The plans' successes in achieving objectives should be measured.'

Measurable outputs should be reviewed for effectiveness and the programme tuned to obtain maximum benefit.

h) 'The objectives and plans should be reviewed as a basis for continual improvement.'

Continual improvement should take the organization forward. Targeting at least a 10 per cent reduction in accidents year-on-year is just as important as maintaining OH&S awareness through new training and refresher courses for the whole workforce.

Risk assessment and control

It is essential that there is a comprehensive appreciation of the significant OH&S hazards and risks associated with the organization, identifying those areas of risk that are unacceptable and putting in place controls wherever this is deemed to be necessary. Other risks will be covered as part of the priority programme.

BS 8800, 3.5.3 states that:

Where hazards cannot be eliminated the organization should ensure that appropriate and effective risk controls are provided to reduce risks to acceptable or tolerable levels. In high hazard industries, organizations need to ensure that proper attention is given to the high consequence, low probability type event to ensure that adequate control is achieved. It could be that the effort needed to achieve this is disproportionate to that needed for the day-to-day risks of the organization.

Resulting risk management arrangements will vary from organization to organization. They can vary within the time frame of the action plan, requiring an initial significant input at the beginning, which can then be reduced during the monitoring phase.

BS 8800, 3.5.3 provides the following guidelines:

'The planning process should define the arrangements for:

a) ongoing, proactive identification of hazards and assessment of risks to OH&S arising out of the work environment and work activities;'
   It should address all aspects of business activity from the 'front desk' to the contractors who visit the site as part of routine (and non-routine) maintenance services.

b) 'the development and implementation of effective workplace precautions and their associated risk control systems that eliminate hazards or reduce risk;'
   Risk control should be based on initially looking to eliminate the risk at source, then following the protocol, through to the use of PPE as a final resort (see Chapter 6).

c) 'recording the significant details and findings of the risk assessment and making them available to those who need the information.'

Risk management documentation forms an essential tool for audit and training purposes and should be collated and managed.

'A risk assessment should always be carried out, and the control measures implemented, before changes are made to work activities or before new activities commence.'

Risk management should be ongoing, not just a one-off exercise. It should be reviewed periodically when changes occur to the process, new processes are introduced (this may require a completely new risk assessment) and after an adverse event, e.g. an accident, incident or ill health occurrence.

Risk assessment should be carried out throughout the organization as this is a legal requirement in the UK (see Chapter 6 for further information).

Legal and other requirements

BS 8800, 3.5.4 states:

> … establish and maintain arrangements to ensure identification and access to all current and emerging legal and other OH&S requirements and guidance relevant to their activities and services. Relevant employees within the organization should be aware of and understand these requirements.
>
> … seek to emulate best practice and performance, in the organization's business sector and other appropriate sources, (e.g. from regulatory agency and trade association guidelines). Best practice guidelines can be of great assistance and arrangements should be made for their identification, dissemination and use.

Best practice guidelines will have been determined from the initial status review. They will need to be included in the planning process to provide mechanisms for identifying changes in legislation which impact on the organization as well as providing early notice of any future changes, e.g. from the EU.

Early notice of these changes can enable organizations to exert influence through consultation processes involving trade associations or by direct comment to regulatory bodies and can support the overall business planning process.

'Other requirements' can include monitoring and implementing industry codes of practice such as the Chemical Industries Association's 'Responsible Care', or a voluntary code such as 'Investors in People'.

OH&S management arrangements

BS 8800, 3.5.5 identifies nine key areas that an OH&S management programme should cover:

a) overall plans and objectives, including employees and resources, for the organization to implement its policy;

b) operational plans to implement arrangements to control the risks identified ... and to meet the recommendations identified ...;

c) contingency plans for foreseeable emergencies and to mitigate their effects (e.g. prevention, preparedness and response procedures);

d) planning for organizational activities ...;

e) plans covering the management of change of either a permanent or temporary nature (e.g. associated with new processes or plant, working procedures, production fluctuations, legal requirements, organizational and staffing changes);

f) plans covering interactions with other interested parties, (e.g. control, selection and management of contractors, liaison with emergency services, visitor control);

g) planning for measuring performance, audits and status reviews ...;

h) implementing corrective actions;

i) plans for assisting recovery and return to work of any staff who is injured or becomes ill through their work activities.

Where fundamental changes cannot be made immediately, prioritized action plans should be drawn up and followed through. In the interim, properly assessed short-term measures should be taken to minimize the risk and the risk assessed over the overall process.

Implementing and documenting

Communication and documented evidence forms an essential part of the planning process. These provide the guidelines for the organization to follow, the records of implementation and the historical record for reviewing the effectiveness of the delivered action against the proposed system.

BS 8800, 3.5.6 states:

> Workplace precautions, risk control systems and management arrangements are more effective if they are well designed and developed recognizing existing business practice. The strength and limitations of human behaviour should be considered in the design.

This is where planning commences. It must deliver a system for successful OH&S management and be clearly understood by the users. Organizations may need to ensure that certain elements of the workforce have a particular academic understanding or at least the confirmed knowledge that they clearly understand the national tongue.

BS 8800, 3.5.6 states:

> All the components of the OH&S management system should be adequately inspected, maintained and monitored to ensure continued effective operation. Risk assessment and risk control should be reviewed in the light of changes and technological developments.
>
> Documentation is vital in enabling an organization to communicate and implement a successful management system. It is also important in assembling and retaining OH&S knowledge. It is important that documentation is:
>
> a) tailored to the organization's needs;
> b) detailed proportionate to the level of complexity, hazards and risks;
> c) kept to the minimum required for effectiveness and efficiency.

Among the most important written communications are:

1) health and safety policy statements;
2) organization statements showing health and safety roles and responsibilities ...;
3) documented performance requirements and measures;
4) supporting organizational and risk control information and procedures;
5) appropriate findings from initial status reviews..., risk assessments investigations..., audits...and periodic status reviews ....

The organization should maintain any records necessary to:

i) demonstrate compliance with legal and other requirements;
ii) ensure retention of appropriate OH&S knowledge;
iii) mitigate any liability claims.

Document systems must be clear and they must be co-ordinated across the organization and maintained, usually as part of the document control system that also applies across the whole of the organization. In some circumstances, particularly where specialist document systems are entering from external sources, the use of a secondary document control process specifically for OH&S management system can be beneficial.

BS 8800:2004, 3.5.6 states:

> Organizations should ensure that sufficient documentation is available to enable OH&S plans to be fully implemented and is proportional to their needs....

Organizations should make arrangements to ensure that OH&S documentation is up to date and applicable to the purpose for which it is intended, takes into account the requirements of data protection legislation and is communicated to all those who need it.

6

Risk assessment and control

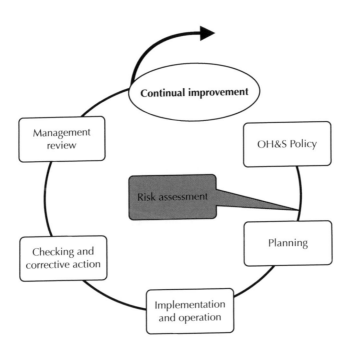

In brief

Risk assessment and control is at the core of effective OH&S management. The process used for risk assessment and control need not be complex and should reflect the type of hazards that exist in the workplace. For instance, there are usually very few hazards in an office environment while there may be many in a chemical or engineering environment. No matter what type of workplace, there is no requirement to address every hazard. The aim should be to identify those hazards that pose a significant risk and therefore need to be addressed rather than trying to eliminate all hazards – a task that is unlikely. It is impracticable to make a workplace totally safe and also be able use it.

The identification of hazards and risk assessment are regulatory requirements throughout Europe and much of the world. Risk assessment is fundamental to the successful application of any health and safety management system. In most instances the process is based on simple principles which can be summarized as follows:

1. Classify work activities.
2. Identify hazards.
3. Identify existing risk controls.
4. Determine risk.
5. Determine acceptability.
6. Prepare risk control action plan to improve risk control as necessary.
7. Review adequacy of action plan – confirm risk acceptability/tolerability.
8. Ensure risk assessment and controls are effective and up to date.

Key elements – Risk assessment and control

Risk assessment is the fundamental element required for the successful implementation of an OH&S management system. It embodies the key principle of proactive management: identifying the hazard and controlling the risk *before* harm occurs and/or damage is sustained to plant, equipment or other operational conditions. The process of identifying hazards, assessing risks and implementing and reviewing risk controls should be the basis of the whole OH&S management system. It is impracticable to make the workplace free of risk but the aim should be to identify and manage all foreseeable risks. In the UK, there is a legal duty on all employers and self-employed people to assess the risks arising from the hazards that result from their work activities. The main purpose of risk assessment is to decide whether existing or planned controls are adequate. This is a proactive process, i.e. controlling risks before harm (or damage) can occur. It is not a one-off exercise, as the measures taken will need to be reviewed from time to time depending on the gravity of the risk and extent of any changes to circumstances. Whenever there is to be any organizational or operational changes a risk assessment should be carried out before the changes are implemented. To ensure that the risk assessment process works, it is essential to involve the workforce and gain commitment to this proactive approach. Risk management should be equally about identifying positive opportunities as it is about avoiding damage or injury.

Risk assessment looks at the risks to which each person is exposed, whether employee, contractor, visitor or anyone else who might suffer harm, and arrives at a judgment as to whether each risk is:

1. acceptable – very low risk where no action is necessary; or
2. low, medium risk – risks in this category should be reduced so that they are acceptable or tolerable, where this is practicable;
3. unacceptable – something needs to be done right away to reduce it (in extreme cases this may involve stopping an activity until new methods or controls can be introduced).

BS 8800, E.1.4 states the following:

> The overall purpose of risk assessment and control is to understand the hazards that might arise in the course of the organization's activities and ensure that any risks to people arising from the hazards are acceptable or tolerable. This is achieved by:

- identifying hazards and making an estimate of the associated risk levels, on the basis of existing or proposed risk controls;
- determining whether these risks are tolerable;
- determining whether further analysis is required to establish whether the risks are, or are not, tolerable, for example noise levels might need to be measured to determine the more exact risk of hearing damage;
- devising improved risk controls where these are found to be necessary.

Risk assessment can also be used to make a systematic comparison of different risk control/reduction options. It aids the organization to prioritize any resulting actions to reduce risk.

It is important that the purpose of risk assessment remains clear in the minds of everyone involved in the process in order to avoid unnecessary work, which is not only wasteful but which might even obscure risks that require urgent attention.

Good judgment, rather than a mechanistic approach, must always be used in assessing a risk. The level of risk attached to almost any action is dependent on whether the relevant controls and safeguards are in place.

Of all the elements of a successful OH&S system, the terminology and understanding is least clear for risk assessment. Similar terminology can apply to the same definition and the difference between the terms 'hazard' and 'risk' is frequently misunderstood. BS OHSAS 18001 specifically defines the key terms:

hazard
source, situation, or act with a potential for harm in terms of human injury or ill health, or a combination of these

hazard identification
process of recognizing that a hazard exists and defining its characteristics

acceptable risk
risk that has been reduced to a level that can be tolerated by the organization having regard to its legal obligations and its own OH&S policy

risk

combination of the likelihood of an occurrence of a hazardous event
or exposure(s) and the severity of injury or ill health that can be
caused by the event or exposure(s)

risk assessment

process of evaluating the risk(s) arising from a hazard(s), taking into
account the adequacy of any existing controls, and deciding whether
or not the risk(s) is acceptable

Definitions of 'risk controls', 'risk control systems', 'unacceptable risk', and
'acceptable risk' are provided within BS 8800.

BS OHSAS 18001, 4.3.1 specifies that the methodology used shall:

a) be defined with respect to its scope, nature and timing to ensure it
   is proactive rather than reactive; and
b) provide for the identification, prioritization and documentation of
   risks, and the application of controls, as appropriate.

For the management of change, the organization shall identify the
OH&S hazards and OH&S risks associated with changes in the
organization, the OH&S management system, or its activities, prior to
the introduction of such changes.

The success of any risk assessment process is based on a systematic approach
being taken. Only then can effective control measures be identified.

Systematic risk assessment and control

This section addresses the fundamentals of managing risk. In order to do this it
is necessary to systematically identify the hazards that are created, assess the
risks and establish what controls (if any) need to be implemented to reduce
the risk of harm to an acceptable level. The process needs to be systematic and
consistently applied, considering all the areas, activities and processes undertaken, in order to avoid missing potential sources of harm.

All organizations differ and the risk assessment process used, whilst having the same eventual aim, will vary from organization to organization. In large, complex operations, the risk assessment may appear complex; in the office environment, the process can be simpler. They will normally be expressed in the form of a documented procedure, although BS 8800, E.1.3 states the following in relation to different risk assessment processes:

Not all of these will necessarily be documented, since there is often a case for managers and employees being trained to make a judgement before work begins or as a response to changing circumstances as to whether there are appropriate risk controls in place. This process is often referred to as dynamic risk assessment.

At the other extreme, there are some systematic documented methods which are complex, and appropriate only to the special circumstances of major hazard activities. For example, risk assessment of a chemical process plant might require complex mathematical calculations of the probabilities of events leading to major release of agents that might affect employees, contractors and others in the workplace, or the public. In many countries, sector-specific legislation specifies where this degree of complexity is required.

The process of risk assessment is based on making a judgment. This often frightens the untrained and inexperienced. The HSE in the UK provides extensive information and guidance to support organizations in their judgment process. The following approach is mainly based on that given in BS 8800 and can be seen as a stepwise, logical approach. There is no right or wrong way and the following methodology is seen as one that any organization can embrace.

1. Classify work activities

List the work activities (including those covering premises, plant, people and procedures) and gather information about them, from start to finish, to include the people they cover, and how they work. The process of classifying work activities should include staff consultation where necessary, as it is often the case that a work activity is carried out differently in practice than it is in theory. It is important that the process includes not only employees but also contractors, visitors and anyone else who might be harmed by the activities of the organization. This does not mean that every person needs to be considered individually. If there are 50 people working in a department, all doing the same thing on identical equipment and under the same conditions, e.g. in a call centre, the hazards are very likely to be the same and one assessment can cover the whole group. Care would, however, need to be taken where, for example, the group includes a new starter who has not been fully trained or someone who has a disability that might put them at greater risk if the premises have to be evacuated.

2. **Identify hazards**

   Identify all significant hazards relating to each work activity, e.g. trapping, slipping, exposure to noise, inhalation of toxic fumes, etc. Consider *who* might be harmed and *how* in relation to the hazard controls that are in place. For each person, or group of people, the key questions to ask are: What could go wrong that could cause injury or damage? Who might be harmed and how? There are hazards in every workplace that will apply to everyone working there as well as visitors and contractors etc., in addition to specific hazards relating to each work activity. A prompt-list of questions relating to hazards is provided on pages 118–119.

3. **Identify existing risk controls**

   Identify the risk controls that exist (or are proposed for planned activities), in order to reduce the risk associated with each hazard. These should be based on the principles of prevention through elimination, substitution, reduction, engineering and, as a final resort, the use of personal protective equipment (PPE) (in that order). Under some conditions, e.g. emergency maintenance, it may be necessary to use a combination of engineering controls and PPE.

4. **Determine the risk**

   Make a subjective estimate of risk associated with each hazard, assuming that planned or existing controls are in place. The assessment should consider the effectiveness of the controls and the consequences of their failure. The style of the assessment should be chosen to best suit the organization and the hazard being assessed. Some organizations use a numerical process for risk assessment; others use descriptive categories such as 'highly unlikely' or 'very probable'. Whichever method is chosen, the aim is to assess the overall risk as being acceptable, minor or serious. Provide a written record where risks are determined to be significant. Defining 'significant' is often difficult. As a rule of thumb, if it takes longer to record a risk assessment than to complete the overall task then the risk is probably not 'significant' and does not need to be recorded.

5. **Determine acceptability**

Decide if the risk is acceptable/tolerable, i.e. that it has been reduced to the lowest level that is reasonably practicable. Judge whether planned or existing OH&S precautions and control measures are sufficient to keep the hazard under control. In order to be able to assess the acceptability of any particular risk, the organization should establish criteria to provide a basis for consistency in all its risk assessments. See BS 8800, E.3.6.

6. **Prepare a risk control action plan**

Deal with any issues that were found by the risk assessment to require attention. Organizations should ensure that new and existing controls remain in place, are effective, are communicated and, where necessary, are recorded. It should be recognized that in some cases, further control measures may not be required.

7. **Review the adequacy of the action plan**

Reassess risks on the basis of the revised controls and check whether risks will be acceptable. This should be done on completion of the plan and periodically during the implementation process until completion. A final review on full implementation should be carried out to ensure suitability and good fit.

8. **Maintenance**

As with the other steps in the process, this review should be documented and repeated periodically to ensure that the controls remain effective. The frequency of the review will be dependent on the risk – the higher the risk, the more frequent the review process. In most circumstances an annual review is recommended. Update and review risk assessments as necessary in order to maintain their validity.

The following checklist identifies the main steps in a risk assessment. A tick box is provided for identifying those procedures that are already in place (1) and those which need to be introduced (2).

CHECKLIST: Risk assessment in the organization

1	2	
❏	❏	Classifying work activities;
❏	❏	Identifying the significant hazards relating to each of these work activities;
❏	❏	Identifying existing risk control measures in place;
❏	❏	Determining the risk associated with each significant hazard;
❏	❏	Deciding if this risk is acceptable/tolerable, i.e. has it been reduced to the lowest level that is reasonably practicable?
❏	❏	Preparing a risk control action plan (if necessary);
❏	❏	Reviewing the adequacy of the action plan – will the risk be acceptable?
❏	❏	Providing a written record where risks are significant;
❏	❏	Periodically reviewing existing risk assessments.

In practice – Risk assessment and control

In terms of risk assessment and control, the six case study organizations have a very similar approach to OH&S management because all of them need to adopt a risk assessment and control system in order to be effective.

The following publications, available from the HSE, provide advice on risk assessment that is applicable to all types of organization:

- The Health and Safety at Work etc. Act 1974, Section 2(2)(b) and Section 6;
- The Management of Health and Safety at Work Regulations 1999;
- INDG163 (rev2), *Five steps to risk assessment;*

There are some risks that affect most organizations. Some examples of these are listed as follows.

a) The reception, clerical and office support environment:
- office chemicals (cleaning solutions) and IT equipment emissions, e.g. from printers, photocopiers;
- electricity and electrical equipment;
- display screen equipment;

- fire and emergencies;
- first aid provision;
- housekeeping and tidiness;
- visiting contractors and the work they undertake;
- manual handling;
- sources of stress, e.g. workload patterns.

b) The structure (all locations, offices, workshops, yards, etc.):
- contractor management, e.g. cleaning windows, servicing heating systems, major repairs and building works;
- workplace condition monitoring and maintenance – welfare facilities;
- security of personnel;
- asbestos and other hazardous materials;
- flammable materials;
- traffic routes;
- space availability;
- lighting levels;
- storage arrangements;
- heating and temperature control (hot and cold);
- site hazards from external sources, e.g. hypodermic needles;
- biological hazards.

c) The processes:
- use of plant and equipment;
- driving;
- planned preventive maintenance and repair;
- emergency maintenance and repair;
- process emissions and body/eye contacts, e.g. dust, fumes, gases, vapours, fibres, mists, liquids, etc.;
- working at height;
- falling objects;
- control measure management;
- electricity;
- ionizing radiation;
- vibration;
- non-ionizing radiation;

- working outdoors – weather effects, e.g. sunburn;
- biological, e.g. contact with rodents, faeces.

The examples described are not exhaustive. Although these key areas will apply in full or in part to every organization, those dealing with highly specialized risks resulting from major hazards like ionizing radiation will need to include these in their risk assessment.

Compliance with specific regulations should be prioritized according to the demands of the business. In the UK, the application of The Management of Health and Safety at Work Regulations 1999, The Electricity at Work Regulations 1989 and The Workplace (Health, Safety and Welfare) Regulations 1992 will assume significant priority in each of the case study organizations, although the risks and the controls that apply have a universal application throughout the world.

In detail – Risk assessment

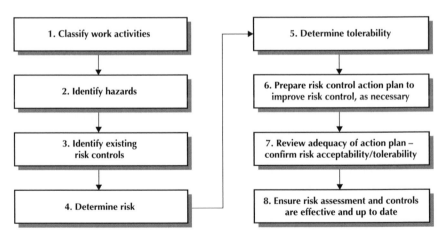

The process of effective risk assessment

Organizations should tailor the approach described here to their own needs, taking into account the nature of their work and the seriousness and complexity of the risks that are present. The full eight-point procedure is not necessary if a preliminary study shows either that the risks are trivial or that the risk controls already in place conform to well-established legal requirements and standards, are appropriate for the task and are understood and used by those involved.

An integrated approach to OH&S risk assessment can be more effective than carrying out separate assessments for, say, health hazards, manual handling hazards, machinery hazards and so on. Not only can separate assessments lead to needless duplication but ranking risk control priorities becomes more difficult if different methods are used.

It is also possible to extend this approach to other management disciplines such as quality assurance, environment, food safety and security. This enables a more encompassing, integrated approach to be adopted for the management system and day-to-day operation of the organization and its activities.

Who carries out the risk assessment?

The skill levels of those assessing the risk and the depth of the programme of risk assessment should reflect the needs of the organization. An office environment is comparatively a much safer place to work than a building site and the assessment should reflect the situation accordingly. In a high risk industry, the assessment of risks is a specialist subject in its own right.

The assessment process should only be undertaken by those persons competent and trained to do so. Knowledge of the process and the risk assessment methodology is essential and a team approach can often be beneficial. Specialist expertise may be required using external resources. The contributory approach requires all of the organization's stakeholders, staff, managers and employee representatives to agree on the most effective way forward. This allows the OH&S procedures:

*   to be based on shared perceptions of hazards and risks;
*   to be necessary and workable;
*   to succeed in preventing harm.

The joint ownership approach can then become part of the overall positive health and safety culture that the organization should be striving to achieve.

Risk assessment requirements

The following checklist shows the requirements necessary for a comprehensive risk assessment programme. A tick box is provided for identifying those procedures/actions that are already in place (1) and those that need to be introduced (2).

CHECKLIST: Requirements for a risk assessment programme

I	2	
❑	❑	Appoint a senior member of the organization to promote and manage the process.
❑	❑	Determine training needs for risk assessment personnel/teams and implement a suitable training programme.
❑	❑	Consult everyone involved; discuss what is planned to be done, obtain their contributions and enable commitment.
❑	❑	Agree the risk assessment process and methodology, including review and approval processes.
❑	❑	Design a simple pro-forma (or use a commercially available version) to record the findings of an assessment appropriate to the organization and the risks involved, including details of the work activity; hazard(s); controls in place; personnel at risk; likelihood of harm; severity of harm; risk levels; action to be taken following the assessment and administrative details, e.g. name of assessor, date of review.
❑	❑	Prepare a delivery plan, addressing significant and high risks as a priority.
❑	❑	Review the adequacy of risk assessment: determine whether the assessment is 'suitable and sufficient' – that is to say, adequately detailed and rigorous.
❑	❑	Document administrative details and significant findings of the assessment in hard copy or electronic form.
❑	❑	Initiate the risk assessment review process periodically, for process change and to ensure that it is suitable.

The process of risk assessment

Stage 1. Classifying work activities

To make the list of activities manageable, the list items should be grouped in a convenient way, e.g. according to:

a) geographical areas within/outside the organization's premises;
b) stages in a production process, or in the provision of a service;
c) planned work, e.g. different operational stages of the process;
d) reactive work, i.e. work carried out in response to an unplanned event;
e) defined tasks, e.g. driving, window cleaning;
f) any change in the management or organization;
g) various identified working groups, e.g. employees, contractors;
h) plant operation and maintenance works;
i) tasks being carried out by contractors.

The following list, though not exhaustive, gives examples of the information required for each work activity. It can be used to prepare a pro-forma checklist tailored to the specific needs of the organization.

1. Tasks being carried out:
   a. duration;
   b. frequency;
   c. external weather condition – wet, cold, hot.
2. Location(s) where the work is carried out.
3. Proximity to and scope of hazardous interaction with other workplace activities, i.e. how one process risk could affect another.
4. Who normally/occasionally carries out the tasks, e.g. operators, maintenance staff.
5. Others who may be affected by the work, e.g. maintenance staff, visitors, contractors, the public, neighbouring organizations.
6. Training that personnel have received in relation to their tasks.

7. Written, safe systems of work and/or permit-to-work procedures prepared for the tasks.
8. Plant, machinery and equipment that is used, e.g. suitability, ease of use.
9. Maintenance, condition, calibration and test condition of plant, machinery and equipment used.
10. Training for plant, equipment and tooling operators.
11. Powered hand tools that are used, e.g. company owned, privately owned.
12. Manufacturers' or suppliers' instructions for operation and maintenance of equipment, plant, machinery and powered hand tools.
13. Size, shape, surface character condition, e.g. sharpness of edges, temperature and weight (including centre of gravity) of materials that will be handled.
14. Physical capabilities of personnel to undertake tasks.
15. Distances and heights that materials have to be moved by hand (including accessibility to loads and environment of transfers).
16. Services used, e.g. electricity, compressed air, gas.
17. Substances used or encountered, e.g. created or given off during a process.
18. Physical form of substances used or encountered (fibre, fume, gas, vapour, liquid, dust/powder, solid).
19. Content and recommendations of safety data sheets relating to substances used or encountered (or formed during a process).
20. Requirements of relevant acts, regulations and standards relevant to the work being done, the plant and machinery used and the substances used or generated during the task.
21. Control measures believed to be in place (and actually in place).
22. Reactive monitoring data – incident, accident and ill health experience associated with the work being done and equipment and substances used, gained as a result of information from within and outside the organization.
23. Findings of any existing assessments relating to the work activity.
24. Other available information, benchmarks, regulatory guidance, professional bodies.

Stage 2. Identifying hazards

There are three key questions in identifying hazards associated with any work activity:

1. Is there a source of harm?
2. Who (or what) could be harmed?
3. How could harm occur?

There are different approaches that can be used to help identify hazards, two of which are given as follows.

Categorizing hazards into broad categories

Here is an example of categorizing hazards by topic:

* mechanical/physical (machinery, plant and equipment);
* electrical (shock, fire);
* substances (chemicals, emissions);
* fire (emergency evacuation, fire fighting equipment);
* explosion (gas, chemical, acts of terrorism);
* temperature/climate (internal/external hot and cold, high humidity);
* radiation (ionizing and non-ionizing, e.g. microwaves);
* biological;
* psychological (stress, work pressures).

Developing a prompt-list of questions

The following example of a hazard prompt-list is not exhaustive and is intended as a starting point for organizations to build up their own list.

During work activities could the following hazard/s exist?

- slips/falls on the level;
- falls of persons from heights;
- falls of tools, materials, etc., from heights;
- inadequate headroom;
- hazards associated with manual lifting/handling of tools, materials, etc.;
- hazards from plant and machinery associated with assembly, commissioning, operation, maintenance, modification, repair or dismantling;
- vehicle hazards, covering both site transport and travel by road (affecting personnel and other vehicles);
- fire, explosion and natural disasters, e.g. earthquakes;
- substances that may be inhaled;
- substances or agents that may damage the eye;
- substances that may cause harm by coming into contact with, or being absorbed by the skin;
- substances that may cause harm by being ingested, i.e. entering the body via the mouth;
- substances that may be injected by a needle or under pressure through broken skin;
- harmful energies, e.g. electricity, noise, vibration;
- radiation – radioactive sources, non-ionizing radiation, sunlight exposure;
- work-related upper limb disorders resulting from frequently repeated tasks;
- inadequate thermal environment, e.g. too hot, too cold, extreme variations in temperature;
- lighting levels (adequacy for tasks or emergencies);
- slippery, uneven ground/surfaces;
- inadequate guard rails or hand rails on stairs;
- contractors' activities;
- violence to staff;
- terrorist activity.

A useful way of gaining the commitment of the workforce as well as ensuring that issues are not overlooked is to involve employees in identifying hazards. This will lead to information on how a task is *actually* carried out rather than how it *should* be done. It should be remembered that the OH&S management system is designed to help the employees and the organization and to establish a workplace where the risk of harm is minimized.

Stage 3. Identify existing risk controls

It is important to establish what controls are in place and how effective they are. The controls may be barriers, light curtains, safe systems of work, lock-out or tag-out procedures, warnings, etc. The evaluation needs to ascertain whether these measures are operating and whether it is possible to improve on them.

Stage 4. Determining risk

The risk from the hazard should be determined by assessing:

- the potential severity of harm; and
- the likelihood that harm will occur.

The assessment can be subjective; it is not essential to assign a numerical value. What is important is that the process enables a sound judgment to be made as to the comparative risk level of different hazards.

It is generally not necessary to make precise numerical calculations of the risks identified. Complex methods for quantified risk assessment are available and are in regular use in those industries where the consequence of failure could be catastrophic, for example nuclear installations. For most organizations, however, much simpler subjective methods are appropriate.

Potential severity of harm

When establishing potential severity of harm, information about the relevant work activity should be considered, together with:

a) part(s) of the body likely to be affected;
b) nature of the harm, ranging from slight to extremely harmful:
  1. slightly harmful, e.g.:
      • superficial injuries; minor cuts and bruises; eye irritation from dust;
      • nuisance and irritation; ill health leading to temporary discomfort;
  2. harmful, e.g.:
      • lacerations; burns; concussion; serious sprains; minor fractures;
      • deafness; dermatitis; asthma; work-related upper limb disorders; ill health;
  3. extremely harmful, e.g.:
      • amputations; major fractures; poisonings; multiple injuries; fatal injuries;
      • occupational cancer; other severely life shortening diseases; acute fatal diseases.

Assigning harm categories will be based on previous experience, the task involved and the overall requirements of the organization. The following table, taken from BS 8800, Annex E, provides examples of harm categories. It emphasizes the ill health aspect with good reason. The number of people per year in the UK dying from ill health arising from exposure to asbestos many years ago, is some 10 times more than those killed in accidents at work. The table can be used as a model and extended to cover groups affected, e.g. contractors, visitors and members of the public. It can also include a welfare category.

Examples of harm categories

Harm category[a] (examples)	Slight harm	Moderate harm	Extreme harm
Health	Nuisance and irritation (e.g. headaches); temporary ill health leading to discomfort (e.g. diarrhoea).	Partial hearing loss; dermatitis; asthma; work related upper limb disorders; ill health leading to permanent minor disability.	Acute fatal diseases; severe life shortening diseases; permanent substantial disability.
Safety	Superficial injuries; minor cuts and bruises; eye irritation from dust.	Lacerations; burns; concussion; serious sprains; minor fractures.	Fatal injuries; amputations; multiple injuries; major fractures.

[a] The health and safety harm categories are effectively defined by quoting examples and these lists are not exhaustive.

Likelihood of harm

When establishing the likelihood of harm, the existing risk controls need to be considered. For specific hazards the legal requirements, codes of practice and guidance from manufacturers/suppliers, etc. are helpful in the assessment. Information may also be available on the number of previous incidents. Further factors to consider are:

a) number of personnel exposed;
b) frequency and duration of exposure to the hazard;
c) failure of services, e.g. electricity and water;
d) failure of plant and machinery components and safety devices;
e) exposure to the elements;

f) protection afforded by personal protective equipment and usage rate of personal protective equipment;

g) unsafe acts (unintended errors or intentional violations of procedures) by persons, for example who:

1. may not know what the hazards are;
2. may not have the knowledge, physical capacity, or skills to do the work;
3. underestimate risks to which they are exposed;
4. underestimate the practicality and usefulness of safe working methods;
5. indulge in horseplay;
6. take short cuts to complete tasks.

It is important to take into account the consequences of all unplanned events. As with the severity of harm, the process of assigning and categorizing likelihood of harm will be designed to meet the organization's needs and the method of doing this is down to each individual organization to decide upon. The following table, from BS 8800, Annex E, provides examples of categories for likelihood of harm, scaled so that the difference between each level alters by a factor of 10. The examples provided in this table can be helpful for maintaining consistency but again, judgment and common sense must be applied. Mechanical assessment must be avoided.

Examples of categories for likelihood of harm

Categories for likelihood of harm	Very likely	Likely	Unlikely	Very unlikely
Typical occurrence	Typically experienced at least once every six months by an individual	Typically experienced once every five years by an individual	Typically experienced once during the working lifetime of an individual	Less than 1% chance of being experienced by an individual during their working lifetime

Stage 5. Deciding if the risk is acceptable

The following table, taken from BS 8800, Annex E, shows one simple method for estimating risk levels and for deciding whether risks are acceptable, i.e. whether the risk has been reduced to the lowest level that is reasonably practicable. In this table, risks are classified according to their estimated likelihood and potential severity of harm. Some organizations may wish to develop more sophisticated approaches, for instance by assigning values instead of terms, although this would not confer any greater accuracy to the estimates.

The matrix shown in the following table is just one approach to assessing risk. The organization can obviously choose a matrix that is larger than this and more accurately reflects the risks associated with its overall activities. Care should, however, be exercised, as a large matrix of, say, 10-by-10 does not imply greater accuracy or greater ability to discriminate between different risks. The approach taken in the table is subjective and, for those organizations with high risks, may be a useful tool in identifying risks that need more careful analytical investigation using sophisticated risk techniques.

A simple risk estimator

Likelihood of harm (see table on page 123)	Severity of harm		
	Slight harm	Moderate harm	Extreme harm
Very unlikely	Very low risk	Very low risk	High risk
Unlikely	Very low risk	Medium risk	Very high risk
Likely	Low risk	High risk	Very high risk
Very likely	Low risk	Very high risk	Very high risk

NOTE These categorizations and the resulting asymmetry of the matrix arise from the examples of harm and likelihood illustrated within this British Standard. Organizations should adjust the design and size of the matrix to suit their needs.

Stage 6. Preparing a risk control action plan

The following table, taken from BS 8800, Annex E, provides a means of establishing a ranking order for risks in the workplace. The aim is to produce an inventory of actions in order of priority. Because the process of ranking is subjective, it is often best for a number of people to be involved in order to ensure the final judgment reflects a balanced view.

This table provides a starting point for deciding the action that should be taken in response to the findings of the risk assessment.

A simple risk-based control plan

Risk level	Tolerability: Guidance on necessary action and timescale
Very low	These risks are considered acceptable. No further action is necessary other than to ensure that the controls are maintained.
Low	No additional controls are required unless they can be implemented at very low cost (in terms of time, money and effort). Actions to further reduce these risks are assigned low priority. Arrangements should be made to ensure that the controls are maintained.
Medium	Consideration should be given as to whether the risks can be lowered, where applicable, to a tolerable level, and preferably to an acceptable level, but the costs of additional risk reduction measures should be taken into account. The risk reduction measures should be implemented within a defined time period. Arrangements should be made to ensure that the controls are maintained, particularly if the risk levels are associated with harmful consequences.
High	Substantial efforts should be made to reduce the risk. Risk reduction measures should be implemented urgently within a defined time period and it might be necessary to consider suspending or restricting the activity, or to apply interim risk control measures, until this has been completed. Considerable resources might have to be allocated to additional control measures. Arrangements should be made to ensure that the controls are maintained, particularly if the risk levels are associated with extremely harmful consequences and very harmful consequences.

Very high	These risks are unacceptable. Substantial improvements in risk controls are necessary, so that the risk is reduced to a tolerable or acceptable level. The work activity should be halted until risk controls are implemented that reduces the risk so that it is no longer very high. If it is not possible to reduce risk the work should remain prohibited.

NOTE   Where the risk is associated with extremely harmful consequences, further assessment is necessary to increase confidence in the actual likelihood of harm.

The next step is to determine what controls need to be put in place for those risks that are not acceptable, taking into account the following:

a)   eliminating hazards altogether, if possible, or combating risks at source;

b)   substitution, e.g. using a safer substance instead of a dangerous one;

c)   if elimination is not possible in trying to reduce the risk, for example by using a low voltage electrical appliance, remote operation from enclosures, or use of refuges to isolate the worker from the hazard rather than relying on PPE;

d)   where possible, adapting work to the individual, for example to take account of individual mental and physical capabilities;

e)   taking advantage of technical progress to improve controls, for example, by using robotics;

f)   use of measures that protect everyone, e.g. having restricted entry areas and using authorized pass mechanisms;

g)   using a blend of engineering, technical and procedural controls;

h)   introducing planned maintenance such as regular extraction system inspection and maintenance;

i)   adopting appropriate PPE, only as a last resort after all other control options have been considered or as a short-term contingency during maintenance or repair;

j)   installing emergency arrangements such as alarm systems and back-up controls;

k)   adopting proactive measurement indicators to monitor compliance with the controls.

Consideration needs to be given to the development of emergency and evacuation plans, and provision of emergency response equipment relevant to the organization's hazards.

The hierarchy should always be to eliminate; remove by substitution; isolate a hazard; control by engineering means and, as a last resort, use appropriate PPE. Sometimes a combination of these measures can be necessary, e.g. in maintenance or emergency situations.

Stage 7. Reviewing adequacy of action plan

Before implementing the new controls, it is important to review the consequences of the proposed action. It is not uncommon to find that there may be new hazards arising from the controls:

- Will the revised controls lead to acceptable risk levels?
- Have new hazards been created?
- Has the most cost-effective solution been chosen?
- What do operators think of the practicality of the preventive measures?
- Will the revised controls be used in practice and not ignored in the face of, e.g. pressures to get the job done?
- How will the revised controls be affected if changes occur to, e.g. plant and machinery, production methods, or the layout of buildings and services?

Stage 8. Ensure risk assessments and controls are effective

A written record should be made where risks are significant. Where action needs to be taken, a record should be kept of the risk assessment and the controls installed. A review date should be included to ensure the corrective measures are reviewed with respect to their effectiveness.

Sample risk assessment form (blank)

Location:

Work Site/activity:

Hazards identified (Please note that serious hazards or conditions of imminent danger must be supported with documented safe systems of work, health and safety plans, etc.)	Persons and/or numbers at risk (indicate numbers or tick where numbers vary)				Severity of harm			Likelihood of harm				Current control measures	Risk rating			
	Employees	Contractors	Visitors	Others (specify)	Extreme harm	Moderate harm	Slight harm	Very likely	Likely	Unlikely	Very unlikely		Very high	High	Low	Very low

NOTES:

Assessor name(s):   Date: Latest review date:

Sample risk assessment form (completed)

Location: Any Town

Work Site/activity: Room 101

Hazards identified (Please note that serious hazards or conditions of imminent danger *must* be supported with documented safe systems of work, health and safety plans, etc.)	Persons and/or numbers at risk (indicate numbers or tick where numbers vary)				Severity of harm			Likelihood of harm				Current control measures	Risk rating			
	Employees	Contractors	Visitors	Others (specify)	Extreme harm	Moderate harm	Slight harm	Very likely	Likely	Unlikely	Very unlikely		Very high	High	Low	Very low
Electricity: electric shock, burns	✓	✓			✓					✓		Electrical equipment and building hard wiring tested in accordance with company procedures. Inspection records provided for equipment and electrical condition status of the building. Only persons trained, competent and authorized are allowed to work on or with electrical equipment systems.	✓			

Managing Safety the Systems Way

Sample risk assessment form (completed)

Location: Any Town
Work Site/activity: Room 101

Hazards identified (Please note that serious hazards or conditions of imminent danger *must be supported with documented safe systems of work, health and safety plans, etc.)*	Persons and/or numbers at risk (indicate numbers or tick where numbers vary)				Severity of harm			Likelihood of harm				Current control measures	Risk rating			
	Employees	Contractors	Visitors	Others (specify)	Extreme harm	Moderate harm	Slight harm	Very likely	Likely	Unlikely	Very unlikely		Very high	High	Low	Very low
Fire: burns, asphyxiation	✓	✓	✓	✓	✓						✓	Fire risk assessment carried out. All employees receive fire safety training. Fire drills are carried out. Fire wardens/evacuation marshals receive training in emergency evacuation/safety procedures. Visitors instructed on emergency procedures on arrival.		✓		

Sample risk assessment form (completed)

Location: Any Town
Work Site/activity: Room 101

Hazards identified (Please note that serious hazards or conditions of imminent danger *must* be supported with documented safe systems of work, health and safety plans, etc.)	Persons and/or numbers at risk (indicate numbers or tick where numbers vary)				Severity of harm			Likelihood of harm				Current control measures	Risk rating			
	Employees	Contractors	Visitors	Others (specify)	Extreme harm	Moderate harm	Slight harm	Very likely	Likely	Unlikely	Very unlikely		Very high	High	Low	Very low
Slips and trips	✓	✓				✓					✓	Floor surfaces kept dry and spillages cleaned up as they arise. Damaged carpet and other surfaces replaced or made safe. Cables and leads kept out of way of walking routes or protected with cable covers. Office housekeeping procedures apply.				✓

NOTES: Others affected by the risk of fire, in addition to employees, contractors and visitors, are neighbours.

Assessor name(s): A.N. Other   Date: 10/11/2004   Latest review date:

Sample risk assessment form completed after implementation of revised control measures

Location: Any Town
Work Site/activity: Room 101

Date: 01/01/2005
Reference: AB 1

Hazards identified (Please note that serious hazards or conditions of imminent danger *must* be supported with documented safe systems of work, health and safety plans, etc.)	Persons and/or numbers at risk (indicate numbers or tick where numbers vary)				Severity of harm			Revised control measures (implemented in addition to current control measures)	Revised likelihood of harm				Revised risk rating			
	Employees	Contractors	Visitors	Others (specify)	Extreme harm	Moderate harm	Slight harm		Very likely	Likely	Unlikely	Very unlikely	Very high	High	Low	Very low
Electricity: electric shock, burns	✓	✓			✓			New electrical equipment included on the location inventory and allocated an inspection date. Routine visual inspection of electrical equipment and service supplies initiated.				✓			✓	
Fire: burns, asphyxiation	✓	✓	✓	✓	✓			Fire alarms fitted. Changes to layouts and/or building fabric made after review of fire risk assessment.				✓				✓
Slips and trips	✓	✓	✓			✓		Maintain through regular housekeeping management.				✓				✓

Assessor (print name):

Approved by (print name):

Risk assessment and control

Sample risk assessment action plan (completed)

Activity/situation hazard	Action required (Note – consider health surveillance requirements, additional engineering controls, personal protective equipment, staff training).	Action date	Action by (name)	Completed by (name)
Electricity	Staff instructed to visually inspect electrical equipment and leads, prior to use, for signs of damage, wear and tear.	1/12/04	Section supervisors	Ongoing
Slips, trips and falls	Clean-up notices posted adjacent to drink dispensing machines.	1/12/04	Canteen supervisor	1/12/04

Name of assessor (print name):

Approved by (print name):

Date of assessment:

Assessor's signature:

Approver's signature:

Assessment review due (date):

Documenting a risk assessment

The way risk assessments are recorded is entirely a matter of choice for the organization. There is a need to identify the site, work area, activity, hazard, those at risk, worst case scenario with respect to harm and the likelihood of harm occurring with the calculated risk rating.

The control measures also need to be identified. The names of those who carried out the assessment should be recorded, preferably along with a date and signature, together with a recommended review date (per risk, if necessary).

A simple example of a blank form is given on the next page. This is followed by a completed version and a further example of a completed form after revised control measures have been implemented, together with an action plan pro-forma.

7

Implementing and operating

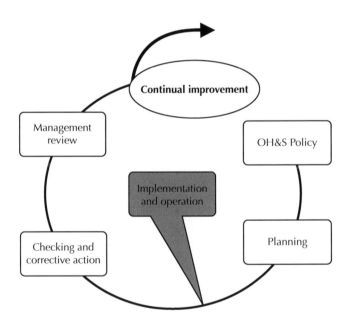

In brief

It's time to start making arrangements for a working system. Having identified in the planning phase what needs to be put in place, all the key areas that must be addressed to make this happen must now be identified.

Key elements – Implementing and operating

For the successful implementation and operation of an OH&S management system, BS OHSAS 18001 identifies seven key areas that need to be addressed.

1. Resources, roles, responsibility, accountability and authority

Top management shall take ultimate responsibility for OH&S and the OH&S management system.

Top management shall demonstrate its commitment by:

a) ensuring the availability of resources essential to establish, implement, maintain and improve the OH&S management system;

… Resources include human resources and specialized skills, organizational infrastructure, technology and financial resources.

b) defining roles, allocating responsibilities and accountabilities, and delegating authorities, to facilitate effective OH&S management; roles, responsibilities, accountabilities, and authorities shall be documented and communicated.

The organization shall appoint a member(s) of top management with specific responsibility for OH&S, irrespective of other responsibilities, and with defined roles and authority for:

a) ensuring that the OH&S management system is established, implemented and maintained ...;
b) ensuring that reports on the performance of the OH&S management system are presented to top management for review and used as a basis for improvement of the OH&S management system.

... The top management appointee (e.g. in a large organization, a Board or executive committee member) may delegate some of their duties to a subordinate management representative(s) while still retaining accountability.

The identity of the top management appointee shall be made available to all persons working under the control of the organization.

All those with management responsibility shall demonstrate their commitment to the continual improvement of OH&S performance.

The organization shall ensure that persons in the workplace take responsibility for aspects of OH&S over which they have control, including adherence to the organization's applicable OH&S requirements (4.4.1).

The most effective OH&S systems are those in which top management shows its commitment and strives for continual improvement by:

• appointing a member of top management with particular responsibility for ensuring that the OH&S management system is properly developed, implemented and supported and performs to requirements in all locations and spheres of operation within the organization;
• providing and maintaining adequate resources essential to the implementation, control and improvement of the OH&S management system and ensuring the competence of those appointed to undertake such tasks;
• directly involving itself in continual improvement measures by 'leading by example';
• developing the management system in line with business development.

2. Training, awareness and competence

OH&S should form a part of all training and awareness requirements for the organization. This should begin at the point of employment by ensuring that staff have the literacy skills and other specific abilities required to carry out a role, e.g. forklift driving, within the required health and safety parameters. These should be confirmed prior to appointment and maintained through refresher training and other competence maintenance and delivery processes.

BS OHSAS 18001 states that:

> The organization shall ensure that any person(s) under its control performing tasks that can impact on OH&S is (are) competent on the basis of appropriate education, training or experience, and shall retain associated records.
>
> The organization shall identify training needs associated with its OH&S risks and its OH&S management system. It shall provide training or take other action to meet these needs, evaluate the effectiveness of the training or action taken, and retain associated records.
>
> The organization shall establish, implement and maintain a procedure(s) to make persons working under its control aware of:
>
> a) the OH&S consequences, actual or potential, of their work activities, their behaviour, and the OH&S benefits of improved personal performance;
> b) their roles and responsibilities and importance in achieving conformity to the OH&S policy and procedures and to the requirements of the OH&S management system, including emergency preparedness and response requirements …;
> c) the potential consequences of departure from specified procedures.
>
> Training procedures shall take into account differing levels of:
>
> a) responsibility, ability, language skills and literacy; and
> b) risk (4.4.2)

In practice this means:

a) employees should have the necessary skills and authority to carry out all their responsibilities in the execution of their duties and be aware of the importance of OH&S in their work delivery;
b) employees should understand the impact that non-compliance will have, along with the added values of compliance;
c) adequate resources should be allocated, taking account of the risks and size of the organization;
d) the skills and competencies needed for the tasks should be identified and any gaps between these and the existing skill profiles should be rectified.

3. Communication, participation and consultation
BS OHSAS 18001 states:

Communication
With regard to its OH&S hazards and OH&S management system, the organization shall establish, implement and maintain a procedure(s) for:

a) internal communication among the various levels and functions of the organization;
b) communication with contractors and other visitors to the workplace;
c) receiving, documenting and responding to relevant communications from external interested parties. (4.4.3.1)

Participation and consultation
The organization shall establish, implement and maintain a procedure(s) for:

a) the participation of workers by their:
   • appropriate involvement in hazard identification, risk assessments and determination of controls;

- appropriate involvement in incident investigation;
- involvement in the development and review of OH&S policies and objectives;
- consultation where there are any changes that affect their OH&S;
- representation on OH&S matters.

Workers shall be informed about their participation arrangements, including who is their representative(s) on OH&S matters

b) consultation with contractors where there are changes that affect their OH&S.

The organization shall ensure that, when appropriate, relevant external interested parties are consulted about pertinent OH&S matters. (4.4.3.2)

It is insufficient merely to instruct or advise on what the organization is striving to achieve. Employees are a very valuable asset. They bring experience to the workplace and often have knowledge of situations which are unknown to their direct supervisors. It is therefore advantageous to involve them in the process of implementing and operating and this should be done from the start. If they own the system, they are more likely to make it work.

4. Documentation

Documents are a fundamental part of an organization's existence. BS OHSAS 18001: states:

The OH&S management system documentation shall include:

a) the OH&S policy and objectives;
b) description of the scope of the OH&S management system;
c) description of the main elements of the OH&S management system and their interaction, and reference to related documents;

d) documents, including records, required by this OHSAS Standard, and

e) documents, including records, determined by the organization to be necessary to ensure the effective planning, operation and control of processes that relate to the management of its OH&S risks.

… It is important that documentation is proportional to the level of complexity, hazards and risks concerned and is kept to the minimum required for effectiveness and efficiency. (4.4.4)

Today it is common to keep documents in electronic format. As with paper-based documentation, however, the aim should always be to ensure that it supports the OH&S system and is not driving it.

5. Control of documents

BS OHSAS 18001, states:

Documents required by the OH&S management system and by this OHSAS Standard shall be controlled …
The organization shall establish, implement and maintain a procedure(s) to

a) approve documents for adequacy prior to issue;

b) review and update as necessary and re-approve documents;

c) ensure that changes and the current revision status of documents are identified;

d) ensure that relevant versions of applicable documents are available at points of use;

e) ensure that documents remain legible and readily identifiable;

f) ensure that documents of external origin determined by the organization to be necessary for the planning and operation of the OH&S management system are identified and their distribution controlled, and

g) prevent the unintended use of obsolete documents and apply suitable identification to them if they are retained for any purpose. (4.4.5)

Records are a special type of document and control over them is dealt with in Chapter 8.

The emphasis should be to ensure that the end-user has access to relevant risk assessment documents and is able to understand their content. This demands a certain level of personal literacy and may even require translation into other languages (e.g. foreign languages, Braille, provisions for those with learning difficulties). When translation is necessary, it is essential to ensure that the translated document fully interprets the original. In some cases, the most effective way is to use pictograms or, where there are many different languages involved, step-by-step diagrams showing how, physically, to carry out certain activities.

The storage of information in electronic form should be reviewed periodically in terms of its permanence and accessibility. Some media such as CDs do not last for ever and changes in software can mean that information becomes inaccessible in the longer term.

6. Operational control

It is essential to implement effective controls to meet any specified requirements for safe operation. BS OHSAS 18001 states:

> The organization shall determine those operations and activities that are associated with the identified hazard(s) where the implementation of controls is necessary to manage the OH&S risk(s). This shall include the management of change ...
>
> For those operations and activities, the organization shall implement and maintain:
>
> a) operational controls, as applicable to the organization and its activities; the organization shall integrate those operational controls into its overall OH&S management system;
> b) controls related to purchased goods, equipment and services;

c) controls related to contractors and other visitors to the workplace;
d) documented procedures, to cover situations where their absence could lead to deviations from the OH&S policy and the objectives;
e) stipulated operating criteria where their absence could lead to deviations from the OH&S policy and objective. (4.4.6)

7. Emergency preparedness and response

Most organizations have some degree of emergency planning in place. This is normally based around the evacuation process but needs to be extended to other areas to ensure that any break in the organization's delivery process causes as little disruption as necessary. BS OHSAS 18001 states:

The organization shall establish, implement and maintain a procedure(s):

a) to identify the potential for emergency situations;
b) to respond to such emergency situations.

The organization shall respond to actual emergency situations and prevent or mitigate associated adverse OH&S consequences.

In planning its emergency response the organization shall take account of the needs of relevant interested parties, e.g. emergency services and neighbours.

The organization shall also periodically test its procedure(s) to respond to emergency situations, where practicable, involving relevant interested parties as appropriate.

The organization shall periodically review and, where necessary, revise its emergency preparedness and response procedure(s), in particular, after periodical testing and after the occurrence of emergency situations. (4.4.7)

Foreseeable emergencies should be identified in the risk assessment process. Contingency plans should include the evacuation of staff and visitors, procedures to interface with the emergency services, and consideration of the provision of start-up arrangements following a major incident. This area is often not adequately addressed in a quality system based on BS EN ISO 9001.

It is important to be able to restart quickly after an emergency as soon as it is safe to do so. There is a standard on business continuity that can help in determining the issues that should be addressed in order to mitigate potential and actual emergencies (BS 25999-2:2007).

The following checklist identifies the key areas in implementing and operating an OH&S management system. A tick box is provided for identifying those procedures that are already in place (1) and those that may need to be introduced (2).

CHECKLIST: Implementing and operating in the organization

1	2	
❏	❏	A member of top management is allocated full responsibility for OH&S throughout the organization and supported by the board.
❏	❏	There is clear responsibility in the management structure.
❏	❏	There is clear accountability in the management structure.
❏	❏	Senior management endeavours to ensure that there is a positive culture towards OH&S.
❏	❏	There is clear delegation of authority in the management structure.
❏	❏	All necessary resources are identified and allocated.
❏	❏	All staff are aware of their individual responsibilities.
❏	❏	All staff are aware of their responsibility to others who may be affected by the activities they control.
❏	❏	All staff are aware of the consequences of their action or inaction.
❏	❏	A training, awareness and competence assessment programme is in place.
❏	❏	A retraining and refresher training programme is in place.
❏	❏	A system for effective, open communication of OH&S information is in place.
❏	❏	Specialist (in-house or external) advice/services are made available, where appropriate.
❏	❏	Employees are fully involved and consulted.
❏	❏	An adequate documentation system is in place.
❏	❏	A system is in place for ensuring documents are kept up to date and relevant.
❏	❏	Contingency plans are in place for emergencies, including arrangements for evacuating the site, liaison with the emergency services and start-up following an emergency.

In practice – Implementing and operating

The case study given in BS 8800, Annex C (Figure C.4) covers the implementation of risk control measures. For the six case study organizations used in this book, there are points of particular reference that helped them to progress. As with previous sections, some of these points will be common to all, while others will be unique to the particular organization.

 ## F&L – office

F&L found that dedicating a key member of staff to occupational health and safety management ensured that OH&S was always on the monthly management meeting agenda. It was able to exercise immediate control over any issues that arose and ensure that risk assessments were carried out before any changes in operations were implemented.

 ## UE – engineering workshop

The wide range of activities undertaken by UE required a large number of procedures and risk assessments. By including the risk assessments with the programme for implementing working procedures and controls, UE was able to ensure that OH&S management was integrated into all its activities. Training staff in the basics of risk assessment has led to a proactive approach to OH&S management, with staff raising issues at an early stage.

UE uses chemicals in its operations and therefore devised a scheme to reduce its use of toxic chemicals and the risk of exposure by moving to lower-risk materials. The simple, routine method used to determine progress was to monitor the stores and designate 'green areas' representing low toxicity, 'yellow areas' representing medium toxicity and 'red areas' representing high toxicity. The output was measured by the space taken up by the three groups. Increases in 'green areas' and reductions in 'red areas' indicated progress in UE's plan.

🛒 LCD – retail

By establishing an emergency plan that included members of the public (at the retail end) and visitors and delivery staff (on the warehouse side), LCD could demonstrate an appropriate level of emergency preparedness. Regular reviews of the system and training of staff, including evacuation drills, ensured its operational effectiveness.

▓▓ B&C – construction

Following the success of restricted employee involvement in the emergency planning arrangements, to which there was a very positive response, it was decided to launch a new initiative involving all staff in reviews of the existing safety management arrangements.

Each site championed a specific safety item on a monthly basis, e.g. handling chemicals and reducing noise, with site and area compliance charted as a league table. Maintaining a safe working environment was used to sell the organization to new customers. B&C also introduced a rigorous management regime to ensure the use of PPE, with non-compliance becoming a disciplinary matter.

YYIMT.com – new technology

As a business relying heavily on the use of display screen equipment, YYIMT identified a need to establish a daily work programme for each display screen equipment user. This ensured that time was being used effectively and also that display screen equipment users had regular breaks away from the equipment. Users also took part in group exercises during their work shift to prevent repetitive strain injury occurring.

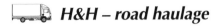 *H&H – road haulage*

Following an incident at one of the sites visited by an H&H driver, the company recognized that it needed to do more than just rely on drivers behaving responsibly behind the wheel. It could not envisage all the situations a driver may face but could provide some basic training on what to do when faced with problems such as 'road rage', hijacking or arriving at a location where it was totally unsafe to unload. The company decided to look at past incidents and talk to the trade association it belonged to, asking for guidance and examples of best practice. A team of drivers led by a senior manager developed some guidance covering various situations. All drivers were briefed and asked for feedback on the proposed guidance. Although H&H recognized that individual drivers would still have to manage any situations they faced, at least they would have the benefit of guidance.

In detail – Implementing and operating

Structure and responsibility

For effective implementation of an OH&S management system, commitment from the highest level in the organization is essential. This commitment is best demonstrated by ensuring that someone at the most senior level within the organization has the specific responsibility for ensuring that the OH&S management system is operating effectively, the arrangements are working in practice and are embedded into the daily activities of the organization.

At every level of the organization, people need to be aware of their responsibilities and to whom they are accountable. They need to recognize the influence that their action or inaction can have on the effectiveness of the OH&S management system. Moreover, the responsibility and accountability for OH&S should be reflected in the management structure. Whether this is documented or not will depend on the size, culture and structure of the organization.

Individual responsibilities

To ensure commitment to OH&S throughout the organization, the following areas need to be addressed.

a) OH&S responsibilities should be clearly defined. Where job descriptions are used it may be appropriate to include OH&S responsibilities as part of them.

b) Personal responsibilities should be reasonable and employees should be given the authority and resources (including time) necessary to carry them out.

c) Appropriate arrangements should exist to ensure that everyone is accountable for discharging their responsibilities.

d) Reporting relationships should be clear and unambiguous.

e) Where personal appraisal systems exist, OH&S performance should be included in the appraisal system.

Everyone in an organization should be aware that, under The Health and Safety at Work etc. Act 1974, 'it shall be the duty of every employee to take reasonable care of himself or any other persons who may be affected by his acts or omissions'. It is not unknown for employees to be prosecuted for their own negligence even when the only person injured is themselves.

It is important to recognize that organizations are responsible for contractors and visitors as well as any other members of the public who attend their business premises and interface with their activities and operations. The OH&S arrangements need to take these factors into account. It is not satisfactory, for example, to employ a firm to clean the premises without ensuring that it is aware of the organization's OH&S arrangements and has its own OH&S arrangements for working at those premises. What this firm does should not compromise the staff of the employing organization and vice versa.

For instance, it is not uncommon to use out-of-hours cleaning staff. In such cases it is essential that the staff are adequately briefed on what they may clean and how they have to clean certain items. They need to be aware of the risks to themselves and the residual risks they may leave behind unwittingly, e.g. unsecured cleaning chemicals that could be used by staff of the employing organization and which might lead to an accident occurring.

When interviewing prospective contractors, it is good practice to find out their attitude to OH&S and to view their OH&S policy and general arrangements. If these can't be provided or there is difficulty in delivering them then there is a real risk that the contractor may cause problems for the employing organization as well as for its own staff. Should an accident occur the employing organization, and in addition the individual responsible for hiring the contractor, may not be able to distance themselves from a contributory responsibility. It needs to be demonstrated that everything reasonably practicable was done to ensure that the contractor was aware of the necessary precautions, procedures, etc. that were in place and that these were verified by the employing organization before allowing work to proceed.

It is also good practice to make sure that staff take responsibility for any visitors they receive, ensuring that, where necessary, they are escorted and protected and do not compromise the organization's OH&S arrangements.

Defining top management responsibilities

The responsibility of top management should include defining the organization's OH&S policy and ensuring that the OH&S management system is implemented. As part of this commitment, top management should designate a specific management appointee with defined responsibilities and authority for implementing the OH&S management system (in large or complex organizations there may be more than one designated appointee). It is preferable that the appointee has some OH&S training and awareness. For board appointees this can be addressed with strategic awareness training covering OH&S and their responsibilities under the Corporate Manslaughter and Corporate Homicide Act 2007.

Defining management appointee responsibilities

Other personnel who have delegated responsibilities for monitoring the overall operation of the OH&S function may support the top management appointee. The management appointee should, however, be regularly informed of the performance of the system and should retain active involvement in periodic reviews and the setting of OH&S objectives. Any other duties or functions assigned to the support personnel should not conflict with the fulfilment of their OH&S responsibilities.

Defining line management responsibilities

Line managers' responsibilities should include ensuring that OH&S is managed within their area of operations. Where prime responsibility for OH&S matters rests with line management, the role and responsibilities of any specialist OH&S function within the organization or brought into it should be appropriately defined to avoid ambiguity with respect to responsibilities and authorities. This should include arrangements to resolve any conflict between OH&S issues and productivity considerations by escalation to a higher level of management for direction.

Documentation of roles and responsibilities

OH&S responsibilities and authorities should be documented in a form appropriate to the organization. This can take one or more of the following forms, or an alternative of the organization's choosing:

- OH&S management system manuals;
- working procedures and task descriptions;
- job descriptions;
- induction training packages.

These should be regularly reviewed to ensure that they meet the organization's needs and are revised to meet new developments and changes in the business, legislation or best practice.

Training, awareness and competence

To ensure an effective OH&S system, it is essential that everyone is competent to take on the duties assigned to them. It is sometimes forgotten that training is as important for those at the highest level in the organization as it is for those at the operational level. Arrangements need to be made for:

a) carrying out a structured training needs analysis, systematically identifying the competencies required by each member of staff (including senior managers) and the training needed to bridge any gap in knowledge and skills;
b) providing any training in a timely and systematic manner;
c) assessing individuals to ensure that they have acquired and are maintaining the necessary knowledge and skills;
d) maintaining appropriate training/skills records;
e) retraining staff as new technologies evolve.

It is important that there are measures in place to ensure that the training is understood and is effective. BS 8800, Annex B.4 provides more information on the specific elements that need to be included in any training programme.

It should be remembered that those not directly involved in core activities also need to be trained. A classic example is those involved in design and development, who need to ensure that the output of their work does not compromise the occupational health and safety of others. If OH&S is not considered at the development stage there can be costly and time-consuming delays later on in the manufacture and operation stages and in maintaining plant and equipment, potentially resulting in client/customer dissatisfaction.

It is easy to forget contractors, temporary workers, trainees and visitors. They all need to be included in any relevant training programme according to the level of risk to which they may be exposed or could themselves cause. Again, it is important to establish the competencies needed for the task. Organizations can put themselves seriously at risk if they do not ensure that they have strived to establish that the contractors they hire are competent for the task they are engaged for.

One way of assessing external competence is through a pre-qualification procedure. This can determine what the organization wants to see demonstrated by its contractors and provides a mechanism for verifying that they have it in place.

Employee involvement and consultation

The commitment of employees throughout the organization to OH&S is essential. They are a valuable asset and source of information in identifying hazards and assessing risk and their cooperation is essential in effectively implementing control measures.

It is not uncommon to find individuals who are well placed to make an important contribution to all aspects of OH&S because, for example, of their training as a safety representative or their past experience. Employees should be encouraged to report shortcomings in the OH&S arrangements and be involved, where appropriate, in the development of OH&S procedures.

There are a number of ways of involving staff and consulting them on OH&S issues. One very effective method is to set up an OH&S committee to act as a vehicle for active participation. Some organizations have found that this can be successfully integrated with other committees dealing with quality, production and environmental issues, thus reducing the possibility of one solution causing problems elsewhere. It is all too easy to resolve a production problem thereby creating a new OH&S problem and vice versa. All too often, the comment is made after the event that 'I could have told you that would have happened but nobody wanted to listen to me'. Actively encouraging employees to share their views and experience avoids this problem and contributes to ensuring compliance.

Communication

Effective communication is a key factor in ensuring delivery of a successful OH&S management system. Arrangements need to be made for:

a) identifying and receiving relevant OH&S information from outside the organization, e.g. changes in legislation, information on new developments and clients' requirements;
b) ensuring that any pertinent OH&S information is communicated to those within the organization who need to know;
c) ensuring that relevant information, e.g. design risks, is communicated to people outside the organization who require it;
d) encouraging feedback and suggestions from staff on OH&S matters – information should be escalated up the organizational chain of command and also across the organization and specific directions should be given to employees and other persons affected;
e) ensuring that lessons learnt from incidents, near misses and accidents are communicated and acted upon;
f) ensuring that management makes it clear that it wants to hear bad news as well as good news – this feedback is essential if it is to take positive action quickly.

Specialist advice and services

Employers are required, with limited exceptions, to appoint one or more competent persons from within or outside the organization to help in applying the provisions of OH&S legislation.

This may be achieved by various means, including training staff from within the organization, engaging trained professionals as in-house employees, e.g. a health and safety officer, or by using the services of competent external consultants to assist with OH&S compliance. Whatever route is chosen, it is essential that adequate information, time, resources and co-operation are available to any specialist adviser. Remember, however, that the employment of an OH&S adviser does not relieve the management of the organization of their legal responsibilities.

OH&S management system documentation

There is always going to be a need for retaining and managing some documentation (hard copy or computer-based) in the OH&S management system. This should reflect the particular needs of the organization and should support the OH&S management system, not drive it. The required documentation should be readily available, simple and understandable and should be maintained.

Organizations with five or more employees are required to have a written statement of OH&S policy and a record of the significant findings of any risk assessment. There is, however, little point in producing a large manual if it is not going to be understood and used by those who have to refer to it. The aim should be only to document what is required, ensuring it is focused on the needs of the user. Consulting those directly involved can be helpful in formulating the structure and wording of any documentation.

Document control

All documentation, records and procedures should be kept up to date and readily accessible to those who are required to use the information. Arrangements need to be made for:

a) keeping accessible records of essential documentation and ensuring backup of electronic versions in the event of IT system failure;

b) assigning responsibility for keeping documents up to date;

c) ensuring that up-to-date information is readily available and communicated to the users;

d) ensuring that information is understandable (bearing in mind the literacy, capability of understanding and mother tongue of the intended users);

e) providing archive arrangements and for managing obsolete documents.

Operational control

To ensure effective operational control, two issues need to be addressed: responsibility (as discussed previously) and integration.

OH&S activity, in its broadest sense, needs to be fully embraced both within and between functions in order to encourage close co-operation and collaboration between all parts of the organization.

All too often, accidents occur because there is a lack of clarity as to who is responsible when areas interface closely with each other. For example, a series of small business units within the same organization may share premises and have their own effective OH&S arrangements for their own workshop, office, etc. but fail to implement any arrangements for a shared delivery yard or the reception area. Often, the OH&S arrangements for 'support' activities, e.g. maintenance staff, cleaners, etc. are inadequate or overlooked.

Encouraging co-operation can be achieved in a number of ways, including:

a) OH&S project teams/task groups comprising representatives from and working with different parts of the organization;
b) managers, OH&S specialists, safety representatives and safety committees addressing problems common to different parts of the organization;
c) co-ordinating OH&S audits and reviews to examine findings and investigate recommendations and remedial actions in an effective manner;
d) inspections, safety surveys and safety tours – these should be focused on those areas where there is a known risk, e.g. housekeeping, ladder inspections, etc. – which shows commitment and ensures that all staff recognize the importance attached to such issues.

Emergency preparedness and response

Contingency plans need to be established to mitigate the effects of any emergency that might affect the organization. It is increasingly recognized that it is essential organizations manage emergencies rather than hope they don't happen. Even very small organizations need to identify the risks of an emergency occurring and understand how they will address it. Equally, all organizations, large and small, want any emergency to interfere with their business delivery systems as little as possible and, in the event of a break in production occurring, be able to recover as quickly as possible. Nowadays it may be important to make provision for employees travelling abroad as they may be subject to local illness and sickness, terrorist activity or kidnap – these scenarios were hardly regarded as a major issue a few years ago but are worthy of consideration in the current climate of globalization.

As well as assessing the risks posed by their own operations and practices, organizations need to be aware of hazards posed by neighbours that may affect their own site. It is important to remember that emergency planning should go beyond evacuation and dealing with the incident. Organizations need to return to normal working as soon as possible so they need to put in place plans for minimizing disruption following an emergency evacuation. Areas to be considered include:

a) recovery of software for information technology systems, ensuring secure storage, containment;
b) safe recovery of undamaged plant and equipment from the original site;
c) maintaining the OH&S management system at temporary sites;
d) reviewing the operation of the OH&S management system in the light of the emergency to identify and remedy any areas of failure so as to prevent a reoccurrence;
e) contingency OH&S plans for contingency arrangements.

The following checklist sets out arrangements that should be considered in a contingency plan for emergencies. A tick box is provided for identifying those that are already covered (1) and those that should be considered (2).

CHECKLIST: Contingency planning for emergencies

1	2	
☐	☐	Identify all potential emergencies that could reasonably be predicted to occur on the site (remembering the activities of neighbours and vandals) or to employees working off-site;

- ❑ ❑ Train staff to deal with off-site emergencies;
- ❑ ❑ Evacuate staff and visitors, alert neighbours;
- ❑ ❑ Alert the emergency services;
- ❑ ❑ Appoint a senior person to co-ordinate and liaise with the emergency services and staff during evacuations and to activate appropriate contingency plans;
- ❑ ❑ Ensure that procedures, equipment, etc. are in place for dealing with emergencies;
- ❑ ❑ Notify the emergency services of any risks they face on the organization's premises, e.g. chemical storage, gas shut-off valves, etc.;
- ❑ ❑ Train staff for evacuations and organized assembly;
- ❑ ❑ Ensure that there is contingency planning for re-mobilization after the emergency, including OH&S management and other essential interface management arrangements, e.g. environmental management requirements.

8

Checking

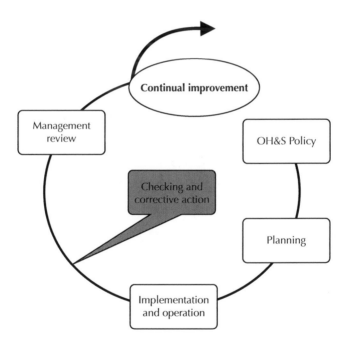

In brief

'What you can't measure, you can't manage' – it's time to put in place procedures to measure and monitor the OH&S system, enabling the organization to put right any deficiencies and to identify opportunities for improvement.

Key elements – Checking

It is essential that systems are put in place to show that the OH&S management system is working and delivering the performance that the organization is committed to achieve. The old adage that 'what you can't measure, you can't manage' very much applies. The organization needs to plan for measuring, checking and correcting any deficiencies.

To ensure an effective checking and correcting stage in an OH&S management system, BS OHSAS 18001 identifies five areas that need to be addressed.

1. Performance measurement and monitoring

… establish, implement and maintain a procedure(s) to monitor and measure OH&S performance on a regular basis. This procedure(s) shall provide for:

a) both qualitative and quantitative measures, appropriate to the needs of the organization;
b) monitoring of the extent to which the organization's OH&S objectives are met;
c) monitoring the effectiveness of controls (for health as well as for safety);
d) proactive measures of performance that monitor conformance with the OH&S programme(s), controls and operational criteria;
e) reactive measures of performance to monitor ill health, incidents (including accidents, near-misses, etc.) and other historical evidence of deficient OH&S performance;

f)   recording of data and results of monitoring and measurement sufficient to facilitate subsequent corrective action and preventive action analysis.

If equipment is required to monitor or measure performance, the organization shall establish and maintain procedures for the calibration and maintenance of such equipment, as appropriate. Records of calibration and maintenance activities and results shall be retained. (4.5.1)

This text is fairly explicit and requires little addition. It should be noted, though, that although qualitative measures are subjective, they can play an important role in measuring performance.

2. Evaluation of compliance

Consistent with its commitment to compliance … establish, implement and maintain a procedure(s) for periodically evaluating compliance with applicable legal requirements.
     … keep records of the results of the periodic evaluations.
     NOTE The frequency of periodic evaluations may vary for differing legal requirements.
     … evaluate compliance with other requirements to which it subscribes. The organization may wish to combine this evaluation with the evaluation of legal compliance … or to establish a separate procedure(s).
     … keep records of the results of the periodic evaluations.
     NOTE The frequency of periodic evaluation may vary for differing other requirements to which the organization subscribes. (4.5.2)

This is a new requirement in BS OHSAS 18001. The intent is that organizations need to keep under review their continuing compliance. It supports the commitment made in the policy statement and the procedures established to ensure compliance.

There are no fixed rules. Periodic reviews can be initiated by several different drivers: changes to legislation, new legislation, business changes, new best practice, an adverse event report or when set by the organization against a key performance indicator. Review periods can also be set according to the activity or business risk. The greater the risk, the more frequent reviews may be required.

3. Incident investigation, nonconformity, corrective action and preventive action

Incident investigation

… establish, implement and maintain a procedure(s) to record, investigate and analyse incidents in order to:

a) determine underlying OH&S deficiencies and other factors that might be causing or contributing to the occurrence of incidents;
b) identify the need for corrective action;
c) identify opportunities for preventive action;
d) identify opportunities for continual improvement;
e) communicate the results of such investigations.

The investigations shall be performed in a timely manner.
… The results of incident investigations shall be documented and maintained.

Nonconformity, corrective action and preventive action

… establish, implement and maintain a procedure(s) for dealing with actual and potential nonconformity(ies) and for taking corrective action and preventive action. The procedure(s) shall define requirements for:

a) identifying and correcting nonconformity(ies) and taking action(s) to mitigate their OH&S consequences;

b) investigating nonconformity(ies), determining their cause(s) and taking actions in order to avoid their recurrence;

c) evaluating the need for action(s) to prevent nonconformity(ies) and implementing appropriate actions designed to avoid their occurrence;

d) recording and communicating the results of corrective action(s) and preventive action(s) taken; and

e) reviewing the effectiveness of corrective action(s) and preventive action(s) taken.

Where the corrective action and preventive action identifies new or changed hazards or the need for new or changed controls, the procedure shall require that the proposed actions shall be taken through a risk assessment prior to implementation.

Any corrective action or preventive action taken to eliminate the causes of actual and potential nonconformity(ies) shall be appropriate to the magnitude of problems and commensurate with the OH&S risk(s) encountered.

The organization shall ensure that any necessary changes arising from corrective action and preventive action are made to the OH&S management system documentation. (4.5.3)

The aim should be to find out the fundamental reasons behind any deficiencies before deciding on what action is necessary (see section entitled 'hazardous incident investigation' on pages 171–173, which is based on the approach given in BS 8800). Reactive, short-term solutions, although expedient, may not address the root cause and can result in further difficulties in the longer term. The recommended methodology is well known and can be related to the model for a successful health and safety management system as shown in the diagram in the Foreword of this book.

Regulations can also require that certain records be retained for a stipulated period, e.g. enforcement bodies may want to review inspection records for local exhaust ventilation equipment and UK statutory provision places responsibility on employers to retain the results of health surveillance for 40 years.

4. Records and records management

... establish and maintain records as necessary to demonstrate conformity to the requirements of its OH&S management system and of this OHSAS Standard, and the results achieved.

... establish, implement and maintain a procedure(s) for the identification, storage, protection, retrieval, retention and disposal of records.

Records shall be and remain legible, identifiable and traceable. (4.5.4)

Implementing a document control system enables an organization to demonstrate how information is cascaded and managed throughout the business. It should be designed in such a way that it is simple and information is easily recovered.

It is essential to recognize that there may be a need to keep records for the working life of employees. Many occupational health complaints are latent and the effects of a short-term exposure to a hazardous substance may develop over a long period of time. Retaining records for the working life of employees may be necessary to comply with a statutory requirement, for example the retention of personal health surveillance records for at least 40 years, or to meet the organization's own personnel management policy.

5. Internal audit

This is covered separately in Chapter 9.

The following checklist sets out the key issues (other than auditing) for checking and correcting the OH&S management system. A tick box is provided for identifying those arrangements that are already in place (1) and those that need to be introduced (2).

CHECKLIST: Checking and correcting in the organization

1	2	
❑	❑	Regular measurement of OH&S performance;
❑	❑	Regular inspections are carried out on equipment and working practices;

- ❑ ❑ Use of proactive measures of performance – such as training and review of risk controls;
- ❑ ❑ Use of reactive measures of performance – such as monitoring accident reports;
- ❑ ❑ Monitoring OH&S performance to ensure objectives and targets are being met;
- ❑ ❑ Where performance is not meeting criteria, identifying the root causes and taking appropriate corrective action;
- ❑ ❑ Investigating accidents and incidents and implementing any corrective and preventive actions;
- ❑ ❑ Keeping OH&S records, particularly those relating to compliance with legal and other requirements, results of audits and reviews.

In practice – Checking and correcting

By its very nature, the output from performance monitoring is very specific to each organization and will vary with time. There are, however, some useful points of reference from the five case study organizations.

 ## F&L – office

Office activities often do not readily lend themselves to checking and monitoring of OH&S performance. F&L overcame this by encouraging the recording and investigation of all accidents and near-miss incidents. This enabled it to identify any adverse trends in specific activities and, by reviewing individuals' work practices, it was able to take action across all activities where this was appropriate.

These arrangements revealed a number of minor injuries in the mailroom. A junior member of staff was required to log and process all the incoming mail before the partners arrived each morning. The urgency of this work and the resulting pressure placed on the member of staff was identified as the root cause of the problem. To overcome the situation, F&L arranged for earlier delivery of the mail to allow extra time for the mail room and it also arranged for assistance to be provided in the final 30 minutes before the mail was needed. Although monitoring past events is a reactive measure, this nonetheless enabled F&L to produce a proactive response to prevent reoccurrence and contribute to safe systems of work.

 ## UE – engineering workshop

In a manufacturing environment a strict regime of checking and monitoring OH&S performance is vital. Regular safety inspections by UE's supervisory staff were used to check that safe systems of work were being operated. Findings were reported at both management and staff level, together with proposed improvements and/or remedial actions. Implementation of improvements was always monitored and the effectiveness of controls measured. In one example the mandatory use of all machinery guards, the clear identification and accessibility of emergency stop buttons on machines and regular inspections to ensure that safeguards were not compromised, for instance, as part of a refined start-up procedure, prevented the possibility of entanglement incidents occurring on machinery.

 ## LCD – retail

Handling deliveries and shelf stacking are a key part of LCD's activities, covering machine handling, the use of forklift trucks and manual handling by individual employees. These operations are prone to vehicle–person incidents and lifting and handling injuries. There is also the possibility of customer injuries caused by badly stacked products, overloaded display stands and the carrying of heavy 'cut loads' from the store to the car park area. By frequent assessment of the following control procedures LCD was able to implement a regime of proactive control measures:

- keeping traffic routes clear and well maintained;
- ensuring lifting aids are always available, suitable for their intended purpose and used by staff;

- reviewing stacking procedures through store layouts and staff training as well as checking and inspection of racking with load notices;
- providing a store customer help service for accessing items and transporting them to customer vehicles.

Frequent programmed inspections ensured that the process was always implemented.

▦ *B&C – construction*

Construction sites have always presented one of the most difficult management environments. This arises from the wide scope of work carried out and the extensive transient workforce employed. By including OH&S as part of site managers'/supervisors' daily responsibilities for managing building activities, breaches of site safety rules and failure to use personal protective equipment (either at all or properly) were dealt with immediately. Findings were also included in daily toolbox talks to re-emphasize the OH&S message and were reviewed regularly to identify areas of repetition at other B&C sites.

YYIMT.com – new technology

YYIMT assigned team leaders with the responsibility for managing OH&S performance within their own particular sectors of the call centre, with the call centre manager acting in a co-ordinating role and addressing areas that were not covered by a team leader. Strict monitoring of workstation layout for display screen equipment was enforced, with the aim of getting employees to manage this crucial area of major risk for the organization. As part of their responsibilities at the end of each day, employees were required to leave workstations organized and set up for the next day or shift period so as to instil discipline and reinforce a safe working environment.

🚚 H&H – road haulage

H&H recognized that maintaining excellent driving skills was its major challenge. This extended to loading activities using forklift trucks, sales representatives who provided the company's commercial input and the hauliers themselves. Accidents could occur under a wide range of circumstances:

- forklift drivers overloading pallets, unbalanced loads, driving too fast, reversing without due care and attention, lack of interaction with site pedestrians and other drivers, poor internal road surfaces and blind areas, use of mobile phones while driving;
- commercial representatives working excessively long hours and travelling long distances, tight time schedules, burden of office duties, RTAs (road traffic accidents);
- hauliers working long hours, stress due to long periods spent away from the home base, RTAs, carriage of dangerous cargoes, tight delivery timescales.

To address these conditions, H&H devised and managed a strict transport policy. This covered all aspects of driving activity, from advanced driver training to addressing road rage, and the inspection and maintenance of all internal road/yard surfaces on a weekly basis.

Each week line and middle managers reviewed all vehicle accident reports together with any subsequent investigations. Reports were also provided at board level on a monthly basis.

In detail – Checking

To ensure that the OH&S management system is operating as envisaged at the planning stage, it is essential to check the performance of the system on a regular basis and to correct any deficiencies that are found.

The checking and correcting stage should deal with the following key questions from the planning stage:

1. Has the *plan* been fully implemented?
2. Have the *objectives and targets* been achieved?
3. Are they still relevant?

In addition, to maintain effective control of specific risks:

4. Are risk controls continuing to be *effective?*
5. Are lessons *being learnt and acted upon* from any OH&S management system deficiencies including hazardous events (accidents, incidents)?
6. Is the information obtained used in reviewing and improving the practices and arrangements?

Monitoring and measurement

Both proactive and reactive monitoring should be used in any performance measurement system to monitor the extent to which the policy and objectives are being met. They also play complementary roles in the control of specific risks.

The control plan should include the proactive monitoring of risk controls. Proactive data, e.g. workplace and documentation inspections, should be used to monitor compliance with risk controls. It should also be used in subsequent risk assessments.

The control plan also needs to include reactive monitoring. Reactive monitoring data, e.g. accident, incident and hazardous event investigation reports, helps with:

a) making subjective estimates of the likelihood and consequences of hazardous events;
b) selecting appropriate risk controls;
c) improving existing practices.

Reviewing existing performance provides a positive response. The use of proactive data as a sole indicator of performance is, however, insufficient. It is quite possible that the training of, for example, forklift truck drivers has increased yet the number of incidents may still be on an upward trend. Evidence from both proactive and reactive monitoring (and from operational experience and local knowledge) should therefore be used to review and, if necessary, improve the controls in place (implement a safe system of work) and compliance with the OH&S management system generally.

Selecting indicators

To determine whether objectives are being met it is necessary to measure performance against them by using monitoring data as measurable performance indicators. BS 8800 specifies the use of 'leading' and 'lagging' performance indicators.

A 'leading' performance indicator is based on data about compliance or non-compliance with a specific performance requirement in the OH&S plan (such as a safe system of work) and compliance with the OH&S management system generally.

A 'lagging' performance indicator is based on data about the prevalence of hazardous events, incidents, accidents, and occupational ill heath.

Accident and ill health data are vital as the final check on the effectiveness of the OH&S management system. For various reasons, however, organizations need to be cautious about their use and they should never be used as the sole measure of OH&S performance.

A combination of leading performance indicators using mainly proactive monitoring data, and lagging performance indicators using mainly reactive monitoring data should be used to assess the overall performance of the OH&S management system.

Examples are given in the following checklist of leading performance indicators and lagging performance indicators using proactive and reactive monitoring data respectively. The list is not intended to be comprehensive. A range of indicators and performance measures should be selected and developed to suit the organization's chosen objectives and information needs. A tick box is provided to help identify those that are already being used (1), those the organization may wish to consider (2) and those that do not apply (3).

CHECKLIST: Performance measures

1	2	3	Examples of leading performance indicators
☐	☐	☐	Progress in achieving the plans, targets and objectives that have been set;
☐	☐	☐	Results of attitude surveys of employee perceptions about management commitment to OH&S;
☐	☐	☐	Appointment of a director with management responsibility for OH&S;
☐	☐	☐	Appointment, where necessary, of OH&S specialist staff – in addition to the safety manager;
☐	☐	☐	Appointment of worker safety representatives or representatives of employee safety who are able to operate effectively;
☐	☐	☐	Monitoring the extent of influence of OH&S specialist staff;
☐	☐	☐	Progress on reviewing and publishing an OH&S policy relevant to company activity;
☐	☐	☐	Progress on communicating the OH&S policy – response and feedback;
☐	☐	☐	Number of personnel trained in OH&S;
☐	☐	☐	Monitoring the effectiveness of OH&S training;
☐	☐	☐	Staff understanding of risk control;
☐	☐	☐	Staff attitude to risks and risk controls;
☐	☐	☐	Progress in completing/regularly reviewing the risk assessment programme;
☐	☐	☐	Monitoring compliance with risk controls;
☐	☐	☐	Monitoring compliance with statutory requirements;
☐	☐	☐	Awareness of new standards and legislation that affect the business;
☐	☐	☐	Monitoring the number and effectiveness of OH&S audits, tours, inspections/surveys;
☐	☐	☐	Monitoring the quality and number of staff suggestions for OH&S improvements;
☐	☐	☐	Monitoring staff attitudes to risks and risk controls;
☐	☐	☐	Monitoring staff understanding of risks and risk controls;
☐	☐	☐	Maintaining agreed housekeeping standards;
☐	☐	☐	Progress on completing and closing out OH&S audits;
☐	☐	☐	Progress on implementing OH&S audit recommendations;
☐	☐	☐	Monitoring the frequency and effectiveness of OH&S committee meetings;
☐	☐	☐	Monitoring the frequency and effectiveness of staff OH&S briefings;
☐	☐	☐	Progress on OH&S specialist reports;
☐	☐	☐	Progress on implementing action on complaints and suggestions;
☐	☐	☐	Results of health surveillance reports;
☐	☐	☐	Results of personal exposure sampling reports, e.g. noise surveys;
☐	☐	☐	Results of workplace exposure level reports, e.g. noise, dust, fumes;
☐	☐	☐	Monitoring the availability and use of PPE;
☐	☐	☐	Implementing engineering controls in place of PPE.

Some examples of measurement techniques are given in the following checklist. A tick box is provided to help identify those that are already in use (1), those the organization may wish to take into account (2) and those that do not apply (3).

CHECKLIST: Examples of measurement techniques

1	2	3	
☐	☐	☐	Systematic workplace inspections using checklists;
☐	☐	☐	Safety tours – for example on a 'walk through' basis;
☐	☐	☐	Inspections of specific machinery and plant to check that safety-related parts are fitted, being used and are in good condition;
☐	☐	☐	Safety sampling – examining specific aspects of OH&S;
☐	☐	☐	Environmental sampling – measuring exposure to substances or energies and comparing with recognized standards;

☐ ☐ ☐	Behaviour sampling – assessing workers' behaviour to identify unsafe working practices that might require correction, for example by work design improvements or through training;
☐ ☐ ☐	Attitude surveys of personnel at all levels;
☐ ☐ ☐	Analysis of documentation and records;
☐ ☐ ☐	Benchmarking against good OH&S practices in other organizations.

Hazardous incident investigation

BS OHSAS 18001 emphasizes the investigation of 'incidents', irrespective of whether or not these gave rise to 'accidents' involving actual injury, ill health or fatality. In practice, there is a natural concern and motivation for organizations to investigate accidents more thoroughly than incidents. However, there are often many precursory incidents (also referred to as near misses, dangerous occurrences, etc.) before accidents causing harm occur.

Identifying the root cause of incidents rather than finding someone to blame who was involved in the actual failure is very important. It is estimated that 80 per cent of accidents are caused by management failure in some way. Hence, the identification of a simple cause may not improve overall performance. Only by understanding what the management failures are within the organization can real performance be addressed in a positive manner.

There are very few occasions in which harm occurs which could not have been foreseen and therefore prevented. Similar events may have occurred within the organization before but, because either harm did not occur or there was no knowledge about the possibility of harm, preventive action was not taken. For instance, 'Jack slipped on the floor and broke his ankle' is a foreseeable incident, particularly if the floor is often wet and many others have slipped but have avoided injury.

For every serious accident there are, typically, 300 minor incidents. This is why it is very important to understand the root cause of incidents in which, although actual harm did not occur, the situation could have had far more serious consequences. This type of incident is often referred to as a near miss, near hit, close call or dangerous occurrence. A brick falling from height on to someone's head is an 'accident' but the brick missing someone's head by a metre is a 'near miss'.

A very comprehensive form is supplied at the end of this chapter, which should help when investigating such events.

There are a number of factors that can be the root cause; it is rare to have just one. The factors can be broken down into three groups:

1. Personal factors – lack of or inappropriate skill, knowledge, competence, behaviour, etc.
2. Job factors – inappropriate environment, equipment, materials, work instructions, etc.
3. Management organizational factors – shortfalls in policy, resources, supervision, assessment of competency and training needs, etc.

The level of investigation should reflect the significance of the event and/or its potential for helping the learning process to improve future conditions. In order to deal with investigations successfully, an organization needs to ensure that staff are available who are either trained or experienced in the required technical and personal skills. The needs should obviously reflect the significance of the event. Equipment such as cameras, tape measures, torches and sample containers may need to be used, together with effective systems of communication, if the site being investigated is hazardous.

The plan of action contained in BS 8800 is a useful checklist of what to cover when investigating hazardous incidents:

- assess risk;
- make safe, make secure, investigate, analyse;
- produce conclusions and recommendations;
- report;
- implement improvements.

Each stage needs to be given careful consideration and the amount of time and effort devoted to the investigation should, if possible, be determined prior to commencement. This should be proportionate to the harm or potential harm caused.

There are important issues to be addressed in such investigations. If the facts are to be established it is very important that those who are interviewed feel they are helping rather than being assessed to establish who can be blamed for the event. The aim of the investigation must be seen as trying to understand and improve rather than to allocate blame.

PERSONAL DETAILS

Name (in full):	Employee number:	DoB: / /	Sex: Male [ ] Female [ ]

Location/department:

Home address:

Telephone number:

Line manager:

Postcode:

Telephone number:

Job description:

Employment: Employee [ ]

Full time [ ] Part time [ ] Self-employed [ ] contractor [ ] passer-by [ ] visitor [ ]

EVENT DETAILS

Date occurred: / /		Time occurred:	
Near-miss incident [ ]	Ill health [ ]	Minor injury [ ]	Serious injury [ ]
Major injury [ ]	Fatality [ ]	Damage only [ ]	RIDDOR reportable [ ]

Injury (including body part, side, injury type)/damage description:

Location/address where event occurred:

How did it happen? (Where appropriate, attach diagrams, photographs, etc.) Include a brief description of events/period leading up to it:

Weather conditions at the time:

Immediate action taken, including action taken to protect others:

First aid treatment: Yes [ ] No [ ] | By whom:

Did the adverse event require the emergency services to be summoned? Yes [ ] No [ ]

Hospital treatment received: Yes [ ] No [ ] | Where:
Details:

Are you able to continue working: Yes [ ] No [ ]

Own job: Yes [ ] No [ ]

Alternative work (give details below):

1 Name(s) of witness(es):	Location:	Tel no.:
2 Name(s) of witness(es):	Location:	Tel no.:
3 Name(s) of witness(es):	Location:	Tel no.:

Employee signature: | Print name:

Completed by (if other than injured person): | Date completed:

Date received by organization's safety representative:

Signature of safety representative:					
Accident/incident status:		Minor [ ]		Major [ ]	
Accident Book Entry/Ref:	Yes [ ]	No [ ]	RIDDOR F2508 Ref:	Yes [ ]	No [ ]
Internal investigation required?	Yes [ ]	No [ ]			

INVESTIGATION

Where did the event happen?	
Who was injured?	
Was there any damage?	
What was being carried out at the time of the event?	
How did the event occur?	

Was there anything unusual about the working conditions when the event occurred?

What was the injury/ill health caused?

If there was a known risk, was a risk assessment in place? (Provide a copy.)

Were there any external influences that contributed to the event taking place, e.g. materials, plant equipment, working environment etc.?

Were the persons present trained/competent to be undertaking their tasks?

Were there any unusual difficulties encountered whilst the work was being undertaken?

Was the activity under any direct supervision?

Were control measures being used as required?

Was personal protective equipment required? (Provide details.)

Was the PPE of the correct type and being used as instructed?

Are there any other factors to be recorded?

ANALYSIS

What are the reasons for the event occurring?

Were there any underlying root causes which led to or contributed to the event?

Has a similar/identical event occurred before? (Provide details, including action taken.)

What new control measures are recommended?

1

2

3

4

Are there similar conditions applying elsewhere which should be investigated?

Which revised control measures should be implemented?

Control Measure	Completion Date	Person Responsible	Completion Confirmed
1			
2			

Which risk assessments, safety plans need to be reviewed – what is required?

Action Plan Risk Assessment/Safety Plan	Completion Date	Person Responsible	Completion Confirmed
1			
2			

Is any further investigation/action required?

Managing Safety the Systems Way

What was the cost of the event – include lost time, production, reporting and investigation involvement, remedial action costs?		
Lost time	**Hours**	**Value (£)**
Production		
Reporting time – all parties	**Hours**	**Value (£)**
Investigation time – all parties	**Hours**	**Value (£)**
Direct remedial action costs	£	
Indirect remedial action costs	£	
Other costs	£	
Details:		

Who needs to be advised of the findings and recommendations?

Person	Position	Date Completed
1		
2		
3		

Is a review required?

When?	By who?
Investigation carried out by: (state all parties)	
Signed:	

9

Auditing

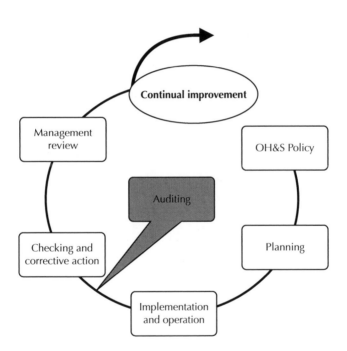

In brief

Organizations need to periodically reassure themselves that the OH&S system is effective and is being followed throughout. It's time to put in place a system of independent internal audits. Auditing is a powerful proactive tool for determining whether the organization is actually carrying out in practice what it has stated it will do. Internal audits should be viewed positively, as a way of ensuring that all is working well and for determining where improvements can be made.

Key elements – Auditing

A system for routinely monitoring OH&S performance is insufficient in itself to ensure that the OH&S management system is effective. There needs to be a procedure for auditing the system to make sure that it is being followed throughout the organization. Only in this way will it be possible to judge whether the system is adequate to meet the requirements expressed in the stated policy of the organization. If it is found that the policy and objectives are not being met then the organization cannot be sure whether it is the system or its implementation that is responsible for the shortfall unless an audit confirms that the system is, in fact, being followed.

Guidance on auditing can be found in BS EN ISO 19011:2002. Although this document is primarily aimed at auditing quality and environmental systems, the principles contained in it apply to the audit of management systems in general. Guidance is also given in *Auditing the 19011 Way* [18] and *Continual Improvement through Auditing* [19].

BS OHSAS 18001, 4.5.5 specifies:

… shall ensure that internal audits of the OH&S management system are conducted at planned intervals to:

a) determine whether the OH&S management system:
    1) conforms to planned arrangements for OH&S management …;
        and

2) has been properly implemented and is maintained; and
3) is effective in meeting the organization's policy and objectives;
b) provide information on the results of audits to management.

Audit programme(s) shall be planned, established, implemented and maintained by the organization, based on the results of risk assessments of the organization's activities, and the results of previous audits.
Audit procedure(s) shall be established, implemented and maintained that address:

a) the responsibilities, competencies, and requirements for planning and conducting audits, reporting results and retaining associated records; and
b) the determination of audit criteria, scope, frequency and methods.

Selection of auditors and conduct of audits shall ensure objectivity and the impartiality of the audit process.

To achieve this in practice requires that the operation of the system is checked in all areas and applications, by auditors who are not directly involved.
The term 'auditing' is frequently misinterpreted by those who are going to be audited, largely because of the association with financial auditing, which is quite different. It is important that the purpose of auditing is made clear to all who are going to be involved as otherwise there may be resentment at a lot of people, probably comparative strangers, asking questions about how a system is being operated. The object is not to find fault. The purpose is to help, not to criticize. If an area is found where the system is not working properly then the reason has to be established. Is the system itself at fault, making it unworkable in some way? Has the manager or operative not understood what is being asked, possibly through lack of training? The auditor is not a policeman but instead more like a coach who tries to find out what is wrong in order to put it right.
Although the main purpose of auditing is to check that the system is being followed and is effective, it is also a primary means of achieving continual improvement of the system, another essential requirement.

If the audit is to be done by employees of the organization (in most cases the best way) then they need to be selected with care and given the training they need. This will consist of training in systems auditing in general and of OH&S systems in particular. If there are experienced quality systems auditors in the organization then they may well be suitable for the task after training on the specialist OH&S aspects. An essential requirement is that those performing the audit do not themselves have direct responsibility for the function being audited, otherwise the integrity of the audit may be compromised.

All parts of the system need to be audited regularly – customarily in the course of a year – but not all parts of the system need to be audited at the same time or at the same frequency. Those areas where the risk is greatest should be audited more frequently than those where the risk is lower and the audit programme should recognize this requirement. Those organizations in which the risks are inherently high should audit their systems more frequently than the annual cycle that is appropriate to other organizations. In areas where the system has been changed, it is advisable to arrange an audit soon after the changes have been fully implemented so that any problems arising can be identified and solved.

Apart from the auditor's independence and integrity, it is important that the auditor feels they have the full support of senior management and can make their findings known to the local manager (if that has been agreed at the commencement of the audit) without being intimidated. The outcome should be confidential to the manager but given freely as a guide to where the system has weaknesses or could be improved. In the absence of such openness, auditors may feel their job is on the line if they deliver bad news. Audits are for the benefit of the organization, to help it improve, and should not be seen as the justification for a 'witch hunt'.

Ideally, the results of audits should be communicated to all relevant personnel on completion of the audit so that any necessary corrective action can be taken and improvements made. These results will be an important input to the annual management review. If the auditor finds a serious problem in the course of the audit this should immediately be raised with the appropriate manager without waiting for the formal report.

The following is a checklist of the key issues in auditing the OH&S management system. A tick box is provided for identifying those issues that are already being addressed (1) and those that need to be considered (2).

CHECKLIST: Auditing in the organization

I	2	
❑	❑	Regular, periodic audits of the OH&S management system are taking place;
❑	❑	Staff conducting audits are competent to perform this task;
❑	❑	Staff conducting audits are independent from the activity being audited;
❑	❑	Audits verify that the organization is fulfilling its OH&S obligations;
❑	❑	Audits identify strengths and weaknesses in the OH&S management system;
❑	❑	Audits verify that the organization is achieving its OH&S performance targets;
❑	❑	Audit results are communicated to all relevant personnel;
❑	❑	Audit results are the basis for corrective action;
❑	❑	Audit results are monitored to ensure OH&S improvement, i.e. there are no repetitions of failures revealed by previous reports.

In practice – Auditing

The six organizations used in our case studies all have similar requirements to audit their OH&S management systems, although the way this is done may differ from one organization to another. One may adopt a horizontal approach such as auditing the application of training programmes in the engineering workshop while another may adopt a vertical approach, such as auditing all the safety management programmes operated by the retail organization. The depth and detail of the audit should be appropriate to the organization. The low risk environment of a business such as F&L (office environment) or YYIMT (new technology-based organization) means that their audit arrangements can be simple.

In contrast, a business such as UE (engineering) or B&C (construction) has more diverse operations and activities, the risks are greater and the audit process will need to be more detailed. For LCD (retail), the audits should address the workforce–customer interface to ensure a safe environment for both groups.

H&H (road haulage) needs to pay special attention to its maintenance activities as this is perceived to be an area that poses risks to its fleet operation with respect to safety and reliability. In addition to auditing its own system, YYIMT also undertook to audit its suppliers to ensure that specific aspects were being properly managed, particularly compliance with food hygiene requirements.

In detail – Auditing

Auditing is an essential element of the OH&S management system. All personnel must appreciate its importance and all managers must be fully committed to it, co-operating in its execution and acting reasonably and promptly on any findings and recommendations. Staff must recognize that it is not a threat but a means of seeing how the system is working and where it needs to be improved. Everyone must co-operate fully and be open and honest with the auditor. In summary, the audit must be seen as an integral part of the process of maintaining and improving the OH&S system.

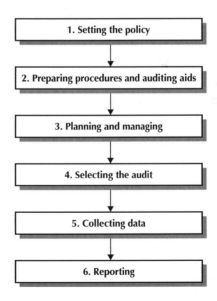

The stages in establishing an audit system

Stage 1. Setting the policy

In developing an audit policy, the issues which need to be considered include:

a) the objectives and purpose of auditing;
b) the standards, procedures and aids to be used;
c) who is to undertake audits (or be part of a team) and the training needed;
d) the arrangements for managing the audit, including budget provisions;
e) formulating the audit programme;
f) the format of audit reports and arrangements for responding to them;
g) performance standards for planning and implementing the audit programme and arrangements to monitor it;
h) arrangements for the review of the audit policy, its implementation and its revision, as necessary.

Stage 2. Preparing procedures and auditing aids

Establishing a procedure for the audit will assist in ensuring that the audit is undertaken efficiently and smoothly. Although the staff being audited will recognize its importance, they may also perceive it as time-consuming and possibly intrusive. It is therefore important that the audit is well organized and focused on the issues at hand. A well-prepared audit will determine the facts quickly and give a productive output that will quickly show the benefits of the system to those involved.

Issues to consider in preparing for the audit are:

a) the elements of the audit process, preparation, on-site work and follow-up programme;
b) the key elements of the OH&S management system, any other topics that the audit programme will address and the criteria against which perform-ance will be judged;
c) a means of ensuring that the audit includes a representative sample of activities to be included;

d) how key questions should be framed;

e) the need for auditing aids, e.g. checklists, *aides-mémoire*, inspection procedures.

The audit system should be based on current best practice and be appropriate to the nature and complexity of the organization.

Stage 3. Planning and managing

Audits cost money. Apart from the direct cost of the auditors (even if they are in-house staff who have been seconded to do the audit) all staff and managers will be involved, so there is a significant indirect cost arising from the disruption and distraction from people's normal duties. It is important therefore that there is a senior manager in charge who is responsible for planning and managing the audit and control of the agreed financial budget for the audit.

The programme and frequency of audits should be appropriate to the nature of the hazards, the degree of risk, the size of the operation, etc. As experience is gained, the records of previous audits will show where problems have arisen in the past and where the emphasis should be placed in future audit programmes. Planning should cover:

a) preparing the programme;

b) the scope of the audit;

c) establishing terms of reference;

d) establishing a timetable;

e) selecting an appropriate audit team.

Stage 4. Selecting the audit team

It is a requirement of any management system standard that all employees are competent to perform the tasks that they are expected to do. If, as is suggested, the audits are to be carried out by members of staff as a part-time occupation separate from their principal duties then it is almost certain they will need training, both in the principles of systems auditing and in the specific disciplines to be audited, in this case occupational health and safety. Even more important is the selection of the right type of person to carry out the audits. If not presented correctly, auditing, as previously stated, can be seen as intrusive as well as disruptive. The auditor must not be seen as an inquisitor who is trying to find faults but more as a coach or mentor who is trying to see if any problems have arisen so that they can be avoided in future. If the audit is seen by everyone as being helpful and constructive it will be of much greater value to the organization.

The auditor must be able to communicate effectively with others at different levels within the organization. One way of achieving this is for each departmental manager to audit a department other than their own. This may bring added benefits to the organization as managers appreciate and understand the workings of other departments. If the organization already has staff who are experienced in auditing the quality system then they can readily be trained to cover the requirements of occupational health and safety. Staff from personnel or training departments may also be suitable for training as auditors – it is their understanding of the organization that is important rather than the specific job role they hold within the organization.

Stage 5. Collecting data

There are a number of stages involved, including:

a) carrying out structured interviews with key personnel throughout the business area to determine that robust procedures are in place and that they are understood and are being followed;

b) examining accident and incident reports for the area;

c) examining other relevant documentation, including policy statements, risk assessment reports, audit records, manuals, etc.;

d) confirming the statements made by observation and examining documents;
e) analysing and interpreting the data;
f) maintaining records.

The auditor should always be looking not only for problems (a term preferable to 'non-compliances' as it sounds less judgmental) but should try to establish the root causes of any problem and discuss with the auditee how these can best be overcome. The audit process can be one of the main means of achieving continual improvement but this depends on the correct relationship being established and preserved between the auditor and the auditee.

If the auditor meets a situation that requires urgent attention then the departmental manager should be told immediately.

Stage 6. Reporting

For each department or section audited, the auditor should prepare a written report. This should be in a standard format and should specify the processes audited, the problems found and details of the actions agreed to overcome them together with names and dates. The auditor and the person responsible for the activity should both sign the report to indicate mutual agreement on the facts of the situation and any remedial actions.

The report should then be passed to the audit manager or whoever is in charge of the process. The audit manager may accept responsibility for checking that the necessary corrective action has been taken to ensure no reoccurrence of the problems that have been reported, or this may be left with the individual auditors to clear with the appropriate managers.

More importantly, the audit manager will be able to judge from the reports received on all the departmental audits whether or not the system is working satisfactorily (there will always be some problems reported but if these are not numerous or serious, the system may be considered to be working) and this will be the basis for the report to top management on the audit as a whole, to be considered as part of the management review. This review will consider whether the system is meeting the requirements of the organization, a question that can only be discussed once the audit has established that the system is indeed in full operation.

10

Reviewing

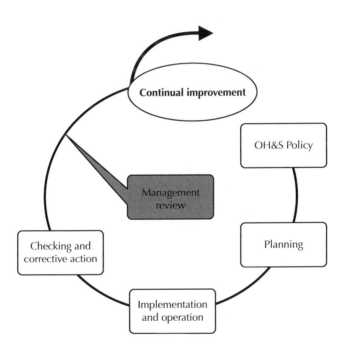

In brief

It's time to take stock of the OH&S management system. The management review is the opportunity for top management to carry out a strategic review of the system at planned intervals to decide if any improvements need to be made. This should take place at least once a year. It should consider any feedback from interim reviews, audits, incidents, inspections and employee consultation, as well as information from external sources (such as regulators, trade associations and insurers). Where improvements will benefit the system and can sensibly be made these need to be taken on board and any required actions communicated.

Key elements – Reviewing

Reviewing management systems is a fundamental requirement in any organization. It ensures that processes and procedures are being applied effectively, as intended, and continue to meet the needs of the organization. Most importantly, it provides the mechanism to drive the continual improvement required of any management system. It is a live process within the organization and is addressed in BS 8800 by the periodic status review and the management review process. In order to ensure a robust OH&S management system, BS OHSAS 18001, 4.6 requires the following:

> Top management shall review the organization's OH&S management system, at planned intervals, to ensure its continuing suitability, adequacy and effectiveness. Reviews shall include assessing opportunities for improvement and the need for changes to the OH&S management system, including the OH&S policy and OH&S objectives. Records of the management reviews shall be retained.

BS OHSAS 18001 identifies specific inputs to the management review and what is expected in the form of outputs. This reinforces the vital role of these reviews in driving the continual improvement cycle required for an effective OH&S management system.

Input to management reviews ... include

a) results of internal audits and evaluations of compliance with applicable legal requirements and with other requirements to which the organization subscribes;
b) the results of participation and consultation;
c) relevant communication(s) from external interested parties, including complaints;
d) the OH&S performance of the organization;
e) the extent to which objectives have been met;
f) status of incident investigations, corrective actions and preventive actions;
g) follow-up actions from previous management reviews;
h) changing circumstances, including developments in legal and other requirements related to OH&S, and
i) recommendations for improvement. (4.6)

'Changing circumstances' referred to in (h) includes both internal and external factors, such as takeovers or mergers, reorganizations, new technology, new projects, etc.

The outputs from management reviews ... consistent with the organization's commitment to continual improvement and ... include any decisions and actions related to possible changes to:

a) OH&S performance;
b) OH&S policy and objectives;
c) resources; and
d) other elements of the OH&S management system.

Relevant outputs from management review ... made available for communication and consultation.

A frequent misconception is that the management review is carried out annually. It should be carried out at least once a year by organizations seeking to demonstrate to a certifying body that the BS OHSAS 18001 system is operating effectively. In reality, the frequency is determined by circumstances. Changing circumstances, accidents, etc. may necessitate more frequent reviews.

To be truly effective, the management review of the organization's processes should be structured around areas of delivery and involve all parts of the organization. This can involve supervisors periodically reviewing OH&S management within a department or over a process or the senior management team considering business performance against the organization's targets, objectives and KPIs (key performance indicators).

The management review differs from the audit in that it is more strategic in its focus. For example, the audit may conclude that everything is in place to meet the OH&S policy and objectives while the management review may show that internal or external considerations justify a change.

As well as seeking to remedy deficiencies, the management review offers the opportunity for a more proactive approach: to consider where the organization wishes to be in managing health and safety issues and how it can maximize the resulting benefits to improve business performance and employee well-being.

The organization should define the frequency and scope of periodic reviews of the OH&S management system according to its needs.

The following is a checklist of the key issues in reviewing the OH&S management system. A tick box is provided for identifying those issues that are already being addressed (1) and those that need to be considered (2).

CHECKLIST: Reviewing OH&S in your organization

1	2	
❏	❏	Top management periodically reviews the OH&S management system;
❏	❏	Business units within the organization undertake reviews of OH&S within their sphere of responsibility;
❏	❏	Management considers the outputs of any periodic status review to identify opportunities for improvement;
❏	❏	The review considers the adequacy, effectiveness and suitability of the OH&S management system;

❑	❑	The review considers performance against annual and local targets and objectives;
❑	❑	The review considers the overall performance of the OH&S management system;
❑	❑	The review considers the performance of the individual elements of the system;
❑	❑	The review considers the findings of audits;
❑	❑	The review considers internal factors affecting OH&S management;
❑	❑	The review considers communications from external parties to the organization;
❑	❑	The review is forward-looking, adopting a proactive approach towards improving the OH&S management system and business performance;
❑	❑	New or revised OH&S objectives are assigned either collectively or to individual functions of the organization that ensure a proactive approach to OH&S management;
❑	❑	The review considers changing circumstances and recommendations for improvement.

In practice – Reviewing

The key to success for each of the case study organizations is how they are managing change relating to OH&S as they evolve and meet changing business and statutory demands. In each case the management review should initiate a proactive response. A significant reactive response is a sign that the OH&S management system may be failing, although in practice most organizations will need to consider both types of response.

 ## F&L – office

For F&L this will be fairly straightforward as it is a relatively small organization but any rapid expansion or a move to larger premises may put strain on its OH&S management system.

For instance, if F&L were to win a new contract with a large client then the sudden increase in workload may have serious repercussions. The potential loss of key staff members through stress-related illness could place the contract at risk and there is also the possibility of permanently losing these staff. F&L needs to be proactive and consider these possibilities at a management review.

The output may be to recruit additional temporary resources or to improve the effectiveness of some of the management processes.

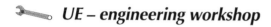 ## UE – engineering workshop

For UE, the situation is totally different. Developments in systems and technology will dictate the pace and management reviews will need to be more regular. The scope for proactive management will often be greater in industries like UE. A new order, for instance, may result in revised shift arrangements and the OH&S arrangements will need to be reviewed to ensure they meet the needs of the changed circumstances.

 ## LCD – retail

Similar to F&L but because of the diversity of its activities and the interface with the public and visitors, LCD will need to be continuously alert to any issues relating to OH&S. The implications of wider issues relating to hygiene and interfacing with all public sectors, e.g. persons with disabilities and young children at retail outlets, may necessitate a fresh look at its practices and what investment/training needs to be considered.

LCD may have to respond, sometimes at short notice, to emerging situations such as balancing accessibility for the public with safety issues. When new merchandising arrives or seasonal events such as Christmas occur, the need for more goods to be stacked and displayed may lead to potential safety issues when there are large numbers of customers. LCD may also need to comply with new legislation regulating the sales of goods to, say, those under the age of 18.

B&C – construction

In the construction industry, the challenge posed by hazardous environments is ever present. While compliance with the CDM regulations and associated legislation is fundamental, the organization needs to learn from how OH&S is successfully implemented from project to project at different work sites. It may need to take account of any best practice being developed and adopted by its competitors.

YYIMT.com – new technology

The IT sector is fast evolving, often providing little time to review previous performance. For YYIMT to succeed commercially and to ensure the effectiveness of its OH&S management system, time has to be allocated to sensibly question and review its OH&S performance. Failure to do so will place the organization at risk of missing even the most fundamental of review benefits.

YYIMT has recently agreed in principle to allow some staff to work at home. It needs to recognize that this is a change in working practice and that the OH&S considerations need to be reviewed. YYIMT may conclude that certain actions need to be taken before the new agreement can be implemented to ensure the facilities at home are suitable.

H&H – road haulage

The competition to H&H was such that they needed to compete at the highest level to remain in business. The adoption of an OH&S management system had brought immediate tangible benefits and the managers were keen to exploit this opportunity even further. Employees had made it known that they were very pleased with the organization's efforts to improve the lifestyle of the drivers, particularly while they were on the road, in terms of improved cab facilities. Absenteeism had decreased and the reliability of H&H's service to customers was much improved. There was still room for improvement and the managers decided employees should be rewarded for their contribution through the OH&S staff suggestion scheme.

In detail – Reviewing

In essence, the management review should consider the overall OH&S management system alongside what the organization is aiming to achieve and decide what further action may be necessary to remedy any shortfalls or move further forward to improve business performance. The main aim should be to identify what future opportunities for improvement there may be, bearing in mind the lifestyle expectation of employees and society, which may directly impinge on the organization.

There are close parallels with the initial status review and the periodic review recommended by BS 8800, in that these aim to determine where the organization is, where it wants to be and how it is going to get there. The management review should be more proactive in seeking ways to minimize risks even further and improve business performance to the advantage of all stakeholders.

The review should not be carried out in isolation from other management discipline review processes as this can be counterproductive. There is little point, for instance, in addressing an OH&S problem with solvent fumes by using extraction to air if this compromises the environmental management system. Under these conditions two elements of control are required, one for OH&S and one for the environment, each demonstrating compliance.

The reviews should take note of such issues as:

1. responses by line supervision to remedy failures to implement workplace precautions and risk control systems which they observe in the course of routine activities;
2. responses to remedy specific examples of substandard performance which are identified by both reactive and proactive monitoring;

3. responses to the assessment of plans and objectives either at the individual, department, site, group or organizational level (see BS 8800);
4. results of any consultation with employees, subcontractors, etc.;
5. responses to dealing with change that could impact on the safe operation of the organization.

The approach should be proactive wherever possible, reviewing developments within the organization, changes in equipment, working practices, etc. at the earliest possible stage (preferably at the planning stage), thus avoiding a reactive response to the control of risks when changes are implemented. Deadlines should be set for implementing changes, responsibilities clearly assigned and implementation monitored. The new arrangements need to be reviewed after they have been operating for a while, to assess their effectiveness and value to the organization.

The following checklist provides a guide (though not exhaustive) to some of the sources of information that the management review should consider. A tick box is provided for identifying those that are already covered (1), those the organization may wish to consider (2) and those believed to be irrelevant (3).

CHECKLIST: Sources of information for consideration in the OH&S management review

1	2	3	Inputs
☐	☐	☐	Information from press reports, health and safety literature, etc.;
☐	☐	☐	Information from health and safety studies;
☐	☐	☐	Findings and recommendations of health and safety audits;
☐	☐	☐	Performance of the overall OH&S system;
☐	☐	☐	Performance of individual elements of the OH&S system;
☐	☐	☐	Changes (present and future) to the organizational structure/staffing levels;
☐	☐	☐	Changes (present and future) to the products/services of the organization (including those provided to the organization);
☐	☐	☐	Changes (present and future) to equipment, plant, buildings, infrastructure, etc.;
☐	☐	☐	Output from OH&S management or other committees;
☐	☐	☐	Information on OH&S performance of similar organizations;
☐	☐	☐	Staff suggestions and concerns;
☐	☐	☐	Risk assessment reviews;

❏ ❏ ❏   Competence reports/training needs;

❏ ❏ ❏   Reports from other key management discipline areas such as quality, environmental, etc.;

❏ ❏ ❏   Trends in accident/incident statistics;

❏ ❏ ❏   Final reviews of completed projects – lessons learnt;

❏ ❏ ❏   Decisions and actions on OH&S performance;

❏ ❏ ❏   Decisions and actions on OH&S policy objectives;

❏ ❏ ❏   Decisions and actions on resources;

❏ ❏ ❏   Decisions and actions on elements of the OH&S management system;

❏ ❏ ❏   Relevant information communicated to interested parties.

11

Integrating your management systems

It is not uncommon for organizations to have a number of management systems operating, some formal and some informal. A difficulty experienced by many organizations is ensuring that the requirements from these separate systems, such as those for managing quality, environment and OH&S, are fully embedded into their operations. Too often they appear as a peripheral attachment. This can lead to conflict and confusion when trying to deal with issues in one discipline independently of others. Such arrangements can be, by their very nature, inefficient and ineffective, particularly if the requirements that are common are handled independently. Every one of these systems should be incorporated and be an integral part of the system for managing the organization.

The manager responsible for the OH&S management system cannot be expected to manage the OH&S risks of the organization in isolation. They should be seen as a support resource to the management team. Managers have many issues they need to manage and these need to be seen as an integral part of the overall management system. Organizations therefore need to recognize that these individual formal management systems are part of this overall management structure. This need not be limited to the fields of quality, environment and OH&S but can also include, for example, financial and human resource management. The aim should be a single defined approach that meets the organization's overall business management needs.

Integration of an OH&S management system can best be achieved by having an integrated business management system or adopting the integrated management system (IMS) approach. Although the IMS approach may seem obvious, there has long been a perceived barrier against progressing towards an integrated system when organizations have adopted formal management systems such as BS EN ISO 9001 or BS EN ISO 14001. This is because the approaches in the documented systems appear to differ and the terms and definitions used have also sometimes been different. This has made it difficult for some organizations to determine what they need to do to make it happen.

In fact, there is no real incompatibility between the systems. Although the needs of every organization differ, adopting the IMS approach should satisfy any organization, no matter what systems they currently operate.

PAS 99, *Specification of common management system requirements as a framework for integration* has been produced for those organizations which have adopted multiple management system specifications. PAS 99 has been produced as a framework, setting out requirements that are commonly found in ISO and BS standards and other consortia specifications such as BS OHSAS 18001. This framework covers many of the requirements found in all of the specifications. The particular needs of the individual specifications still have to be addressed but these, in the term of clause requirements, are a small proportion of the whole. The main requirements can be categorized into the following subjects:

- policy;
- planning;
- implementation and operation;
- performance assessment;
- improvement;
- management review.

By configuring the requirements in the specifications in a common manner it is possible to identify the overlaps and redundancy. This then allows the systems to be interfaced or integrated more readily. The approach is shown in the following diagram, which is based on Figure 1 from PAS 99.

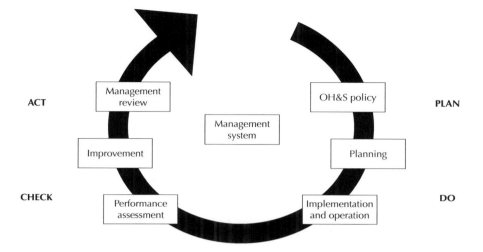

What this shows is that by configuring your existing management systems in such a way that they follow the PAS 99 framework, the common requirements can be integrated to whatever extent the organization so wishes. The specific requirements such as customer focus, environmental aspects, occupational health and safety risks, food safety critical control points, etc. may need to be dealt with separately depending on the complexity of the organization.

The same framework shown in the diagram on page 207 (Figure 2 from PAS 99) can be used as a structure for the implementation of an integrated system or business management system, should the organization choose to go down this route. The model is based on the one originally developed as an 'ideal framework' for standards writers. The background for the use of this model is given in *IMS: A Framework for integrated management systems* [20]. It can be used to control the risks an organization needs to manage in its day-to-day operation.

Such approaches have been adopted by organizations when integrating their own systems. Despite the apparent conflict between the 'process' approach (BS EN ISO 9001) and the 'PDCA' approach (BS EN ISO 14001), organizations have found that the common elements in PAS 99 combined with the process and PDCA approaches, can provide a useful way to effect integration. This model has been successfully implemented in a number of organizations both large and small.

It is suggested that organizations wishing to adopt the IMS approach use one of their existing systems as a starting point. This would normally be the system most established and understood and, perhaps, already subject to certification. This system should be reviewed against Appendix 1, taken from *IMS: A Framework for integrated management systems* [20], and any deficiencies identified and rectified. This then becomes the foundation upon which the other management systems are integrated, using common processes, documentation, etc. as appropriate.

The IMS approach is best followed using a structured time frame and a set of deliverable targets. There may be resistance to the IMS approach, usually from those wishing either to protect or promote the design of their own system. It should be made clear that all elements are working to achieve the same overall aim of the effective and efficient management of the organization.

For information on how BS EN ISO 14001 (environment), BS OHSAS 18001 and BS EN ISO 9001 align with the IMS framework, see Appendix 1.

For those who have followed this book and wish to align their OH&S system, the table on page 208 identifies where the arrangements fit. As stated before, if you have an existing system based on BS EN ISO 14001 or BS EN ISO 9001, it may be best to align them first and then integrate your arrangements within the IMS framework. This table shows where the various clauses sit within such a framework and where specific issues need to be addressed.

PLAN

Management system policy 4.2

Planning 4.3
- **4.3.1** Identification and evaluation of aspects, impacts and risks
- **4.3.2** Identification of legal and other requirements
- **4.3.3** Contingency planning
- **4.3.4** Objectives
- **4.3.5** Organizational structure, roles, responsibilities and authorities

DO

Implementation and operation 4.4
- **4.4.1** Operational control
- **4.4.2** Management of resources
- **4.4.3** Documentation requirements
- **4.4.4** Communication

ACT

Management review 4.7
- **4.7.1** General
- **4.7.2** Input
- **4.7.3** Output

Improvement 4.6
- **4.6.1** General
- **4.6.2** Corrective, preventive and improvement action

CHECK

Performance assessment 4.5
- **4.5.1** Monitoring and measurement
- **4.5.2** Evaluation of compliance
- **4.5.3** Internal audit
- **4.5.4** Handling of non-conformities

Policy

Planning

Implementation and operation

Management review

Improvement

Performance assessment

Management system

General requirements 4.1

Comparison of PAS 99 and BS OHSAS 18001:2007 clauses

Requirements of PAS 99	BS OHSAS 18001:2007
4.1 General requirements	**4.1**
4.2 Management system policy	**4.2**
4.3 Planning	**4.3**
4.3.1 Identification and evaluation of aspects, impacts and risks	**4.3.1**
4.3.2 Identification of legal and other requirements	**4.3.2**
4.3.3 Contingency planning	**4.4.7**
4.3.4 Objectives	**4.3.3**
4.3.5 Organizational structures, roles, responsibilities and authorities	**4.4.1**
4.4 Implementation and operation	**4.4**
4.4.1 Operational control	**4.4.6**
4.4.2 Management of resources	**4.4.1**
4.4.3 Documentation requirements	**4.4.4, 4.4.5**
4.4.4 Communication	**4.4.3**
4.5 Performance assessment	**4.5**
4.5.1 Monitoring and measurement	**4.5.1**
4.5.2 Evaluation of compliance	**4.5.2**
4.5.3 Internal audit	**4.5.5**
4.5.4 Handling nonconformities	**4.5.3**
4.6 Improvement	**4.6**
4.6.1 General	**4.6**
4.6.2 Corrective and preventive action	**4.5.3**
4.7 Management review	**4.6**
4.7.1 General	**4.6**
4.7.2 Input	**4.6**
4.7.3 Output	**4.6**

Appendix 1

Common elements of quality, environmental and OH&S systems

NOTE This table should be taken as a guide only, as correspondence between the clauses is not always precise.

Requirements of PAS 99	ISO 9001:2000	ISO 14001:2004	BS OHSAS 18001:2007
4.1 General requirements	4.1 5.5	4.1	4.1
4.2 Management system policy	5.1 5.3	4.2	4.2
4.3 Planning	5.4	4.3	4.3
4.3.1 Identification and evaluation of aspects, impacts and risks	5.2 5.4.2 7.2	4.3.1	4.3.1
4.3.2 Identification of legal and other requirements	5.3 7.2.1 7.2.2	4.3.2	4.3.2
4.3.3 Contingency planning	5.4 8.3	4.4.7	4.4.7
4.3.4 Objectives	5.4.1 5.4.2 8.5.1	4.3.3	4.3.3
4.3.5 Organizational structure, roles, responsibilities and authorities	5.1 5.5	4.4.1	4.4.1

4.4 Implementation and operation	7	4.4	4.4
4.4.1 Operational control	7	4.4.6	4.4.6
4.4.2 Management of resources	5.1 5.5.1 6	4.4.1 4.4.2	4.4.1 4.4.2
4.4.3 Documentation requirements	4.2	4.4.4 4.4.5 4.5.4	4.4.4 4.4.5 4.5.3
4.4.4 Communication	5.3 5.5.1 5.5.3 7.2.3	4.4.3	4.4.3
4.5 Performance assessment	8	4.5	4.5
4.5.1 Monitoring and measurement	8 7.6	4.5.1	4.5.1
4.5.2 Evaluation of compliance	8.2	4.5.2	4.5.2
4.5.3 Internal audit	8.2.2	4.5.5	4.5.5
4.5.4 Handling of nonconformities	8.3 8.4 8.5	4.5.3	4.5.3
4.6 Improvement	8.5	4.5.3 4.6	4.6
4.6.1 General	8.5	4.5.3 4.6	4.6
4.6.2 Corrective and preventive action	8.3 8.4 8.5	4.5.3	4.5.3
4.7 Management review	5.6	4.6	4.6
4.7.1 General	5.6.1	4.6	
4.7.2 Input	5.6.2	4.6	
4.7.3 Output	5.6.3	4.6	

forthcoming legal requirements. It is important to recognize how legal requirements arise internationally that become enshrined within UK law.

International Laws and Treaties

Convention or Treaty

European Parliament

Directive

United Kingdom Parliament

Health and Safety at Work etc. Act, 1974

Specific Regulations

Approved Code of Practice/Guidance

Company Procedures

How United Kingdom legal requirements evolve

The development of Directives and Regulations in Europe impacts directly on UK requirements in this field and organizations need to be aware of EU developments as they could affect the way they operate in the future.

One way of keeping abreast is to use a CD-based system such as CEDREC that is updated every few months and allows an organization to quickly identify what might apply to it. The HSE website at www.hse.gov.uk/legislation is also useful and has a section dedicated to forthcoming legislation.

Institutions such as those listed below may also help in specific areas:

Institute of Occupational Health IOSH: www.iosh.co.uk/
Royal Society for Prevention of Accidents RoSPA: www.rospa.com/
British Safety Council: www.britishsafetycouncil.co.uk/

The following legal requirements are referenced in this book:

Great Britain (1994) *The Chemicals (Hazard Information and Packaging for Supply) Regulations 1994*, London: The Stationery Office

Great Britain (2007) *The Construction (Design and Management) Regulations 2007*, London: The Stationery Office

Great Britain (2006) *The Control of Asbestos Regulations 2006*, London: The Stationery Office

Great Britain (2005) *The Control of Noise at Work Regulations 2005*, London: The Stationery Office

Great Britain (1980) *The Control of Pollution (Special Waste) Regulations 1980*, London: The Stationery Office

Great Britain (2002) *The Control of Substances Hazardous to Health Regulations 2002 (COSHH)*, London: The Stationery Office

Great Britain (2007) *Corporate Manslaughter and Corporate Homicide Act 2007*, London: The Stationery Office

Great Britain (1995) *The Disability Discrimination Act 1995*, London: The Stationery Office

Great Britain (1989) *The Electricity at Work Regulations 1989*, London: The Stationery Office

Great Britain (1971) *The Fire Precautions Act 1971*, London: The Stationery Office

Great Britain (1995) *The Food Safety (General Food Hygiene) Regulations 1995*, London: The Stationery Office

Great Britain (1974) *The Health and Safety at Work etc. Act 1974 (HASWA)*, London: The Stationery Office

Great Britain (1996) *The Health and Safety (Consultation with Employees) Regulations 1996*, London: The Stationery Office

Great Britain (1992) *The Health and Safety (Display Screen Equipment) Regulations 1992*, London: The Stationery Office

Great Britain (1981) *The Health and Safety (First-Aid) Regulations 1981*, London: The Stationery Office

Great Britain (1996) *The Health and Safety (Safety Signs and Signals) Regulations 1996*, London: The Stationery Office

Great Britain (1972) *The Highly Flammable Liquids and Liquefied Petroleum Gases Regulations 1972*, London: The Stationery Office

Great Britain (1999) *The Ionising Radiations Regulations 1999*, London: The Stationery Office

Great Britain (1998) *The Lifting Operations and Lifting Equipment Regulations 1998 (LOLER)*, London: The Stationery Office

Great Britain (1999) *The Management of Health & Safety at Work Regulations 1999*, London: The Stationery Office

Great Britain (1992) *The Manual Handling Operations Regulations 1992*, London: The Stationery Office

Great Britain (1992) *The Personal Protective Equipment at Work Regulations 1992*, London: The Stationery Office

Great Britain (1989) *The Pressure Systems and Transportable Gas Containers Regulations 1989*, London: The Stationery Office

Great Britain (1998) *The Provision and Use of Work Equipment Regulations 1998 (PUWER II)*, London: The Stationery Office

Great Britain (2005) *The Regulatory Reform (Fire Safety) Order 2005*, London: The Stationery Office

Great Britain (1995) *The Reporting of Injuries, Diseases and Dangerous Occurrences Regulations 1995* (RIDDOR), London: The Stationery Office

Great Britain (1977) *The Safety Representatives and Safety Committee Regulations 1977*, London: The Stationery Office

Great Britain (1992) *The Workplace (Health, Safety and Welfare) Regulations 1992*, London: The Stationery Office

EUROPEAN COMMUNITIES. Council Directive 89/391 EEC of 12 June 1989 on the introduction of measures to encourage improvements in the safety and health of workers at work. Official Journal of the European Communities No. L183/1–8, 12.6.1989

Appendix 4

British standards publications relating to health and safety

This list comprises many of the most used British, European and International Standards, together with other BSI publications. (Please note: this list is not exhaustive and new publications produced by BSI are appearing all the time. Visit www.bsigroup.com for the latest publications and news.) You may find it useful to tick those that are applicable to you (1), those that are not applicable (2) and those that may apply (3).

1	2	3	
☐	☐	☐	BS EN 3, Portable fire extinguishers (all parts);
☐	☐	☐	BS EN 138, 139, 269, Respiratory protective devices;
☐	☐	☐	BS EN 165:2005, Personal eye-protection – Vocabulary;
☐	☐	☐	BS EN 166:2002, Personal eye protection – Specifications;
☐	☐	☐	BS EN 172:1995, Specification for sunglare filters used in personal eye-protectors for industrial use;
☐	☐	☐	BS EN 175:1997, Personal protection – Equipment for eye and face protection during welding and allied processes;
☐	☐	☐	BS EN 250:2000, Respiratory equipment – Open-circuit self-contained compressed air diving apparatus – Requirements, testing, marking;
☐	☐	☐	BS EN 280:2001, Mobile elevating work platforms – Design calculations – Stability criteria – Construction – Safety – Examinations and tests;
☐	☐	☐	BS EN 340:2003, Protective clothing – General requirements;

| 1 2 3

☐ ☐ ☐ BS EN 342:2004, Protective clothing – Ensembles and garments for protection against cold;

☐ ☐ ☐ BS EN 343:2003, Protective clothing – Protection against rain;

☐ ☐ ☐ BS EN 349:1993, Safety of machinery – Minimum gaps to avoid crushing of parts of the human body;

☐ ☐ ☐ BS EN 353-2:2002, Personal protective equipment against falls from a height – Guided type fall arresters including a flexible anchor line;

☐ ☐ ☐ BS EN 354, 355, 360, 361, 362, 364, 365, Personal protective equipment against falls from a height;

☐ ☐ ☐ BS EN 358:2000, Personal protective equipment for work positioning and prevention of falls from a height – Belts for work positioning and restraint and work positioning lanyards;

☐ ☐ ☐ BS EN 367, Protective clothing;

☐ ☐ ☐ BS EN 374:2003 (Parts 1–3), Protective gloves against chemicals and micro-organisms;

☐ ☐ ☐ BS EN 378:2000, Refrigerating systems and heat pumps – Safety and environmental requirements (all parts);

☐ ☐ ☐ BS EN 381, Protective clothing for users of hand-held chain saws (all parts);

☐ ☐ ☐ BS EN 388:2003, Protective gloves against mechanical risks;

☐ ☐ ☐ BS EN 397:1995, Specification for industrial safety helmets;

☐ ☐ ☐ BS EN 407:2004, Protective gloves against thermal risks (heat and/or fire);

☐ ☐ ☐ BS EN 414:2000, Safety of machinery – Rules for the drafting and presentation of safety standards;

☐ ☐ ☐ BS EN 415-3: 2000, Safety of packaging machines – Form, fill and seal machines;

☐ ☐ ☐ BS EN 420:2003, Protective gloves – General requirements and test methods;

☐ ☐ ☐ BS EN 421:1994, Protective gloves against ionizing radiation and radioactive contamination;

☐ ☐ ☐ BS EN 464:1994, Protective clothing – Protection against liquid and gaseous chemicals, including liquid aerosols and solid particles – Test method – Determination of leak-tightness of gas-tight suits (Internal Pressure Test);

☐ ☐ ☐ BS EN 469:2005, Protective clothing for firefighters – Requirements and test methods for protective clothing for firefighting;

☐ ☐ ☐ BS EN 471:2003, High-visibility warning clothing for professional use – Test methods and requirements;

☐ ☐ ☐ BS EN 481:1993 (BS 6069-3.5:1993), Workplace atmospheres – Size fraction definitions for measurement of airborne particles;

☐ ☐ ☐ BS EN 482:2006, Workplace atmospheres – General requirements for the performance of procedures for the measurement of chemical agents;

☐ ☐ ☐ BS 499-1: Supplement: 1992, Welding terms and symbols – Part 1: Glossary for welding, brazing and thermal cutting – Supplement: Definitions for electric welding equipment;

☐ ☐ ☐ BS EN 500-1:2006, Mobile road construction machinery – Safety – Common requirements;

1	2	3
☐	☐	☐	BS ISO 509:1996, Pallet trucks – Principal dimensions;

| ☐ | ☐ | ☐ | BS EN 510:1993, Specification for protective clothing for use where there is a risk of entanglement with moving parts;

| ☐ | ☐ | ☐ | BS EN 511:2006, Protective gloves against cold;

| ☐ | ☐ | ☐ | BS EN 531:1995, Protective clothing for workers exposed to heat;

| ☐ | ☐ | ☐ | DD ENV 581-2:2000, Outdoor furniture – Seating and tables for camping, domestic and contract use – Mechanical safety requirements and test methods for seating;

| ☐ | ☐ | ☐ | BS EN 614-1:2006, Safety of machinery – Ergonomic design principles – Terminology and general principles;

| ☐ | ☐ | ☐ | BS EN 626-1:1995, Safety of machinery – Reduction of risks to health from hazardous substances emitted by machinery – Principles and specifications for machinery manufacturers;

| ☐ | ☐ | ☐ | BS EN 626-2:1996, Safety of machinery – Reduction of risks to health from hazardous substances emitted by machinery – Methodology leading to verification procedures;

| ☐ | ☐ | ☐ | BS 638-4:1996, Arc welding power sources, equipment and accessories – Part 4: Specification for welding cables;

| ☐ | ☐ | ☐ | BS 638-5:1988, Arc welding power sources, equipment and accessories – Part 5: Specification for accessories (Partially replaced by BS EN 60974-12:1996 and BS EN 60974-5:2002);

| ☐ | ☐ | ☐ | BS EN 702:1995, Protective clothing – Protection against heat and flame – Test method – Determination of the contact heat transmission through protective clothing or its materials;

| ☐ | ☐ | ☐ | BS EN 792, Hand-held non-electric power tools – Safety requirements – Fastener driving tools (all parts);

| ☐ | ☐ | ☐ | BS EN 795:1997, Protection against falls from a height – Anchor devices – Requirements and testing;

| ☐ | ☐ | ☐ | BS 807:1955, Specification for spot welding electrodes;

| ☐ | ☐ | ☐ | BS EN 818-7:2002, Short link chain for lifting purposes – Safety – Fine tolerance hoist chain, Grade T (Types T, DAT and DT);

| ☐ | ☐ | ☐ | BS EN 840-6:2004, Mobile waste containers – Safety and health requirements;

| ☐ | ☐ | ☐ | BS EN 863:1996, Protective clothing – Mechanical properties – Test method: puncture resistance;

| ☐ | ☐ | ☐ | BS EN 894-3:2000, Safety of machinery – Ergonomics requirements for the design of displays and control actuators – Control actuators;

| ☐ | ☐ | ☐ | BS 950-1:1967, Specification for artificial daylight for the assessment of colour – Part 1: Illuminant for colour matching and colour appraisal;

| ☐ | ☐ | ☐ | BS EN 976-2:1997, Underground tanks of glass-reinforced plastics (GRP) – Horizontal cylindrical tanks for the non-pressure storage of liquid petroleum based fuels – Transport, handling, storage and installation of single wall tanks;

| ☐ | ☐ | ☐ | BS EN 1052-1:1999, Methods of test for masonry – Part 1: Determination of compressive strength;

| ☐ | ☐ | ☐ | BS 1089:1973, Specification for Workhead spindle noses for grinding machines: cylindrical external, internal and universal types;

1	2	3	
☐	☐	☐	BS 1129:1990, Specification for portable timber ladders, steps, trestles and lightweight stagings;
☐	☐	☐	BS EN 1272:1998, Child care articles – Table mounted chairs – Safety requirements and test methods;
☐	☐	☐	BS EN 1335-2:2000, Office furniture – Office work chair – Part 2: Safety requirements;
☐	☐	☐	BS EN 1335-3:2000, Office furniture – Office work chair – Part 3: Safety test methods;
☐	☐	☐	BS EN 1417:1997, Rubber and plastics machines – Two roll mills – Safety requirements;
☐	☐	☐	BS EN 1444:2001, Fibre-cement pipelines – Guide for laying and on-site work practices;
☐	☐	☐	BS EN 1537:2000, Execution of special geotechnical work – Ground anchors;
☐	☐	☐	BS EN 1598:1998, Health and safety in welding and allied processes – Transparent welding curtains, strips and screens for arc welding processes;
☐	☐	☐	BS EN 1612-1:1997, Rubber and plastics machines – Reaction moulding machines – Safety requirements for metering and mixing units;
☐	☐	☐	BS EN 1645-1:2004, Leisure accommodation vehicles – Caravans – Habitation requirements relating to health and safety;
☐	☐	☐	BS EN 1647:2004, Leisure accommodation vehicles – Caravan holiday homes – Habitation requirements relating to health and safety;
☐	☐	☐	BS EN 1755:2000, Safety of industrial trucks – Operation in potentially explosive atmospheres – Use in flammable gas, vapour, mist and dust;
☐	☐	☐	BS EN 1845:1999, Footwear manufacturing machines – Footwear moulding machines – Safety requirements;
☐	☐	☐	BS EN 1870-4:2001, Safety of woodworking machines – Circular sawing machines – Multiblade rip sawing machines with manual loading and/or unloading;
☐	☐	☐	BS EN 1870-5:2002, Safety of woodworking machines – Circular sawing machines – Circular sawbenches/up-cutting cross-cut sawing machines;
☐	☐	☐	BS EN 1915-1:2001, Aircraft ground support equipment – General requirements – Basic safety requirements;
☐	☐	☐	BS EN 1949:2002, Specification for the installation of LPG systems for habitation purposes in leisure accommodation vehicles and in other vehicles;
☐	☐	☐	BS EN 1953:1999, Atomizing and spraying equipment for coating materials – Safety requirements;
☐	☐	☐	BIP 2010, IMS: The Excellence Model;
☐	☐	☐	BIP 2011, IMS: Continual Improvement Through Auditing;
☐	☐	☐	BIP 2012, IMS: Risk Management for Good Governance;
☐	☐	☐	BIP 2016, IMS: Managing Food Safety;
☐	☐	☐	BS 2037:1994, Specification for portable aluminium ladders, steps, trestles and lightweight stagings;
☐	☐	☐	BS 2830:1994, Specification for suspended access equipment (suspended chairs, traditional steeplejack's seats, work cages, cradles and platforms) for use in the building, engineering construction, steeplejack and cleaning industries;
☐	☐	☐	BS 2881:1989, Specification for cupboards for the storage of medicines in health care premises;

1	2	3	
❏	❏	❏	BS 3044:1990, Guide to ergonomics principles in the design and selection of office furniture;
❏	❏	❏	BS EN ISO 3457:2003, Earth-moving machinery – Guards – Definitions and requirements;
❏	❏	❏	BS 3632:2005, Residential park homes – Specification;
❏	❏	❏	BS ISO 3776-1:2006, Tractors and machinery for agriculture – Seat belts – Anchorage location requirements;
❏	❏	❏	BS ISO 3776-2:2007, Tractors and machinery for agriculture – Seat belts – Anchorage strength requirements;
❏	❏	❏	BS 4142:1997, Method for rating industrial noise affecting mixed residential and industrial areas;
❏	❏	❏	BS 4163:2007, Health and safety for design and technology in schools and similar establishments – Code of practice;
❏	❏	❏	BS 4211:2005, Specification for permanently fixed ladders;
❏	❏	❏	BS 4422:2005, Fire – Vocabulary;
❏	❏	❏	BS 4465:1989, Specification for design and construction of electric hoists for both passengers and materials;
❏	❏	❏	BS 4676:2005, Protective clothing – Footwear and gaiters for use in molten metal foundries – Requirements and test methods;
❏	❏	❏	BS 5080-1:1993, Structural fixings in concrete and masonry – Part 1: Method of test for tensile loading;
❏	❏	❏	BS 5080-2:1986, Structural fixings in concrete and masonry – Part 2: Method for determination of resistance to loading in shear;
❏	❏	❏	BS 5228, Noise and vibration control on construction and open sites (all parts);
❏	❏	❏	BS 5234-2:1992, Partitions (including matching linings) – Part 2: Specification for performance requirements for strength and robustness including methods of test;
❏	❏	❏	BS 5243:1975, General principles for sampling airborne radioactive materials;
❏	❏	❏	BS 5266-6:1999, Emergency lighting – Code of practice for non-electrical low mounted way guidance systems for emergency use – Photoluminescent systems;
❏	❏	❏	PD 5304:2005, Guidance on safe use of machinery;
❏	❏	❏	BS 5306, Fire extinguishing installations and equipment on premises (all parts);
❏	❏	❏	BS 5330:1976, Method of test for estimating the risk of hearing handicap due to noise exposure;
❏	❏	❏	BS EN ISO 5349-1:2001, Mechanical vibration – Measurement and evaluation of human exposure to hand-transmitted vibration – General requirements;
❏	❏	❏	BS 5395-1:2000, Stairs, ladders and walkways – Code of practice for the design, construction and maintenance of straight stairs and winders;
❏	❏	❏	BS 5395-2:1984, Stairs, ladders and walkways – Code of practice for the design of helical and spiral stairs;
❏	❏	❏	BS 5395-3:1985, Stairs, ladders and walkways – Code of practice for the design of industrial type stairs, permanent ladders and walkways (partially replaced by BS EN ISO 14122-1, -2, -3:2001);

1	2	3
☐	☐	☐	BS 5415-2.2: Supplement no. 1:1986, Safety of electrical motor-operated industrial and commercial cleaning appliances – Particular requirements – Specification for type H industrial vacuum cleaners for dusts hazardous to health;
☐	☐	☐	BS 5426:1993, Specification for workwear and career wear;
☐	☐	☐	BS 5459-2:2000, Specification for performance requirements and tests for office furniture – Office pedestal seating for use by persons weighing up to 150 kg and for use up to 24 hours a day, including type-approval tests for individual components;
☐	☐	☐	BS 5499, Graphical symbols and signs – Safety signs, including fire safety signs;
☐	☐	☐	BS 5588-8:1999, Fire precautions in the design, construction and use of buildings – Code of practice for means of escape for disabled people;
☐	☐	☐	BS 5628-1:2005, Code of practice for use of masonry – Structural use of unreinforced masonry;
☐	☐	☐	BS 5628-2:2005, Code of practice for use of masonry – Structural use of reinforced and prestressed masonry;
☐	☐	☐	BS 5667-1:1979 (ISO 1819:1977), Specification for continuous mechanical handling equipment – Safety requirements – General;
☐	☐	☐	BS 5744:1979, Code of practice for safe use of cranes (overhead/underhung travelling and goliath cranes, high pedestal and portal jib dockside cranes, manually-operated and light cranes, container handling cranes and rail-mounted low carriage cranes) (partially replaced by BS 7121, Parts 1–3);
☐	☐	☐	BS 5944, Measurement of airborne noise from hydraulic fluid power systems and components (all parts);
☐	☐	☐	BS 5974:1990, Code of practice for temporarily installed suspended scaffolds and access equipment;
☐	☐	☐	BS 6037-1:2003, Suspended access equipment;
☐	☐	☐	BS 6037-2:2004, Code of practice for the planning, design, installation and use of permanently installed access equipment – Travelling ladders and gantries;
☐	☐	☐	BS 6132:1983, Code of practice for safe operation of alkaline secondary cells and batteries;
☐	☐	☐	BS 6133:1995, Code of practice for safe operation of lead-acid stationary batteries;
☐	☐	☐	BS 6165:2002, Specification for small disposable fire extinguishers of the aerosol type;
☐	☐	☐	BS 6166-1:1986, Lifting slings – Methods of rating;
☐	☐	☐	BS 6166-2:1986, Lifting slings – Specification for marking;
☐	☐	☐	BS 6166-3:1988, Lifting slings – Guide to the selection and safe use of lifting slings for multi-purposes;
☐	☐	☐	BS 6180:1999, Barriers, in and about buildings – Code of practice;
☐	☐	☐	BS ISO 6393:1998, Acoustics – Measurement of exterior noise emitted by earth-moving machinery – Stationary test conditions;
☐	☐	☐	BS ISO 6394:1998, Acoustics – Measurement at the operator's position of noise emitted by earth-moving machinery – Stationary test conditions;
☐	☐	☐	BS 6458-2.1:1984 (IEC 60695-2-1:1980), Fire hazard testing for electrotechnical products – Test methods – Glow-wire test;

☐ ☐ ☐ BS 6458-2.3:1985, (IEC 60695-2-3:1984), Fire hazard testing for electrotechnical products – Test methods – Bad-connection test with heaters;

☐ ☐ ☐ BS EN ISO 6529:2001, Protective clothing – Protection against chemicals – Determination of resistance of protective clothing materials to permeation by liquids and gases;

☐ ☐ ☐ BS ISO 6534:2007, Forestry machinery – Portable chain-saw hand-guards – Mechanical strength;

☐ ☐ ☐ PD 6576:1995 (CR 1100:1993), Memorandum on health and safety standardization in support of 'New Approach' Directives – Application in the field of machinery;

☐ ☐ ☐ PD 6585-2:1996, Hand-arm vibration – Guidelines for vibration hazards reduction – (CR 1030-2:1995) Management measures at the workplace;

☐ ☐ ☐ BS 6604:1985, Code of practice for safe operation of starter batteries;

☐ ☐ ☐ BS 6626:1985, Code of practice for maintenance of electrical switchgear and controlgear for voltages above 1 kV and up to and including 36 kV;

☐ ☐ ☐ BS 6643-1:1985, Recharging fire extinguishers (manufactured to BS 5423 'Specification for portable fire extinguishers') – Specification for procedure and materials;

☐ ☐ ☐ BS 6643-2:1985, Recharging fire extinguishers (manufactured to BS 5423 'Specification for portable fire extinguishers') – Specification for powder refill charges;

☐ ☐ ☐ BS 6655:1986 (EN 26189:1991, ISO 6189:1983), Specification for pure tone air conduction threshold audiometry for hearing conservation purposes;

☐ ☐ ☐ BS EN ISO 6683:2005, Earth-moving machinery – Seat belts and seat belt anchorages – Performance requirements and tests;

☐ ☐ ☐ BS 6812-3:1991 (ISO 6395:1988), Airborne noise emitted by earth-moving machinery – Method of measurement of exterior noise in dynamic test conditions;

☐ ☐ ☐ BS 6841:1987, Guide to measurement and evaluation of human exposure to whole-body mechanical vibration and repeated shock;

☐ ☐ ☐ BS EN ISO 6942:2002, Protective clothing – Protection against heat and fire – Method of test: Evaluation of materials and material assemblies when exposed to a source of radiant heat;

☐ ☐ ☐ BS 7083:1996, Guide to the accommodation and operating environment for information technology (IT) equipment;

☐ ☐ ☐ BS 7085:1989, Guide to safety aspects of experiments in which people are exposed to mechanical vibration and shock;

☐ ☐ ☐ BS 7121, Code of practice for safe use of cranes (all parts);

☐ ☐ ☐ BS 7135-2:1989 (EN 29295:1991, ISO 9295:1988), Noise emitted by computer and business equipment – Method of measurement of high-frequency noise;

☐ ☐ ☐ BS 7135-3:1989 (ISO 9296:1988), Noise emitted by computer and business equipment – Method for determining and verifying declared noise emission values;

☐ ☐ ☐ BS 7212:2006, Code of practice for the safe use of construction hoists;

☐ ☐ ☐ BS 7255:2001, Code of practice for safe working on lifts;

☐ ☐ ☐ BS 7518:1995 (IEC 61017-2:1994), Radiation protection instrumentation – Portable, transportable or installed equipment to measure x or gamma radiation for environmental monitoring – Integrating assemblies;

1	2	3	
❑	❑	❑	BS 7570:2000, Code of practice for validation of arc welding equipment;
❑	❑	❑	BS 7669-3:1994, Vehicle restraint systems – Guide to the installation, inspection and repair of safety fences;
❑	❑	❑	BS 7671:2008, Requirements for electrical installations – IEE Wiring Regulations – Seventeenth edition;
❑	❑	❑	BS EN ISO 7779:2001, Acoustics – Measurement of airborne noise emitted by information technology and telecommunications equipment;
❑	❑	❑	BS 7801:2004, Escalators and moving walks – Code of practice for safe working on escalators and moving walks;
❑	❑	❑	BS 7863:1996, Recommendations for colour coding to indicate the extinguishing media contained in portable fire extinguishers;
❑	❑	❑	BS 7885:1997, Code of practice for safe entry into silos;
❑	❑	❑	BS 7899-1:1997, Code of practice for assessment of hazard to life and health from fire – General guidance;
❑	❑	❑	BS 7899-2:1999, Code of practice for assessment of hazard to life and health from fire – Guidance on methods for the quantification of hazards to life and health and estimation of time to incapacitation and death in fires;
❑	❑	❑	BS 7963:2000, Ergonomics of the thermal environment – Guide to the assessment of heat strain in workers wearing personal protective equipment;
❑	❑	❑	BS 8081:1989, Code of practice for ground anchorages (Partially replaced by BS EN 1537:2000);
❑	❑	❑	BS 8206-2:1992, Lighting for buildings – Code of practice for daylighting;
❑	❑	❑	BS 8213-1:2004, Windows, doors and rooflights – Design for safety in use and during cleaning of windows, including door-height windows and roof windows – Code of practice;
❑	❑	❑	BS 8216:1991, Code of practice for use of sprayed lightweight mineral coatings used for thermal insulation and sound absorption in buildings;
❑	❑	❑	BS 8800:2004, Occupational health and safety management systems – Guide;
❑	❑	❑	BS EN ISO 9185:2007, Protective clothing – Assessment of resistance of materials to molten metal splash;
❑	❑	❑	BS EN ISO 9241-5:1999, Ergonomic requirements for office work with visual display terminals (VDTs) – Workstation layout and postural requirements;
❑	❑	❑	HB 10190, IMS: The Framework;
❑	❑	❑	HB 10191, IMS: Implementing and Operating;
❑	❑	❑	BS EN ISO 11111, Textile machinery safety requirements (all parts);
❑	❑	❑	BS EN ISO 11611:2007, Protective clothing for use in welding and allied processes;
❑	❑	❑	BS EN 12012-1:2007, Plastics and machines – Size reduction machines – Safety requirements for blade granulators;
❑	❑	❑	HB 10215:2002, CDM Regulations – Procedures manual – 2nd edition;
❑	❑	❑	BS EN ISO 10882-1:2001, Health and safety in welding and allied processes – Sampling of airborne particles and gases in the operator's breathing zone – Sampling of airborne particles;

1	2	3	
❏	❏	❏	BS EN ISO 10882-2:2000, Health and safety in welding and allied processes – Sampling of airborne particles and gases in the operator's breathing zone – Sampling of gases;
❏	❏	❏	BS EN ISO 10993-17:2002, Biological evaluation of medical devices – Establishment of allowable limits for leachable substances;
❏	❏	❏	BS EN 12001:2003, Conveying, spraying and placing machines for concrete and mortar – Safety requirements;
❏	❏	❏	BS EN 12043:2000, Food processing machinery – Intermediate provers – Safety and hygiene requirements;
❏	❏	❏	BS EN 12077-2:1999, Cranes safety – Requirements for health and safety – Limiting and indicating devices;
❏	❏	❏	BS EN 12198-1:2000, Safety of machinery – Assessment and reduction of risks arising from radiation emitted by machinery – General principles;
❏	❏	❏	BS EN 12267:2003, Food processing machinery – Circular saw machines – Safety and hygiene requirements;
❏	❏	❏	BS EN 12268:2003, Food processing machinery – Band saw machines – Safety and hygiene requirements;
❏	❏	❏	BS EN 12492:2000, Mountaineering equipment – Helmets for mountaineers – Safety requirements and test methods;
❏	❏	❏	BS EN 12514-1:2000, Installations for oil supply systems for oil burners – Safety requirements and tests – Parts, oil feed pumps, control and safety devices, supply tanks;
❏	❏	❏	BS EN 12574-3:2006, Stationary waste containers – Safety and health requirements;
❏	❏	❏	BS EN 12811-1:2003, Temporary works equipment – Scaffolds – Performance requirements and general design;
❏	❏	❏	BS EN 13000:2004, Cranes – Mobile cranes;
❏	❏	❏	BS EN ISO 13090-1:1998, Mechanical vibration and shock – Guidance on safety aspects of tests and experiments with people – Exposure to whole-body mechanical vibration and repeated shock;
❏	❏	❏	BS EN 13157:2004, Cranes – Safety – Hand powered lifting equipment;
❏	❏	❏	BS ISO/TR 13387-1:1999, Fire safety engineering – Application of fire performance concepts to design objectives;
❏	❏	❏	BS ISO/TR 13387-8:1999, Fire safety engineering – Life safety – Occupant behaviour, location and condition;
❏	❏	❏	BS EN 13390:2002, Food processing machinery – Pie and tart machines – Safety and hygiene requirements;
❏	❏	❏	BS EN 13557:2003, Cranes – Controls and control stations;
❏	❏	❏	BS EN 13621:2004, Food processing machinery – Salad dryers – Safety and hygiene requirements;
❏	❏	❏	BS EN ISO 13850:2006, Safety of machinery – Emergency stop – Principles for design;
❏	❏	❏	BS EN ISO 14001:2004, Environmental management systems – Requirements with guidance for use;
❏	❏	❏	BS EN ISO 14122, Safety of machinery – Permanent means of access to machinery (all parts);

1	2	3	
☐	☐	☐	BS EN 14175-2:2003, Fume cupboards – Safety and performance requirements;
☐	☐	☐	BS EN 14594, Respiratory protective devices – Continuous flow compressed air line breathing apparatus – Requirements, testing, marking;
☐	☐	☐	BS EN 14605:2005, Protective clothing against liquid chemicals – Performance requirements for clothing with liquid-tight (type 3) or spray-tight (type 4) connections, including items providing protection to parts of the body (types PB [3] and PB [4]);
☐	☐	☐	BS EN 14988-1:2006, Children's high chairs – Safety requirements;
☐	☐	☐	BS EN 14988-2:2006, Children's high chairs – Test methods;
☐	☐	☐	BS EN ISO 15011-2:2003, Health and safety in welding and allied processes – Laboratory method for sampling fume and gases generated by arc welding – Determination of emission rates of gases, except ozone;
☐	☐	☐	BS EN ISO 15025:2002, Protective clothing – Protection against heat and flame – Method of test for limited flame spread;
☐	☐	☐	BS EN 15090:2006, Footwear for firefighters;
☐	☐	☐	BS OHSAS 18001:2007, Occupational health and safety management systems – Requirements;
☐	☐	☐	OHSAS 18002:2000, Occupational health and safety management systems – Guidelines for the implementation of OHSAS 18001;
☐	☐	☐	BS EN ISO 20344:2004, Personal protective equipment – Test methods for footwear;
☐	☐	☐	BS EN ISO 20345:2004, Personal protective equipment – Safety footwear;
☐	☐	☐	BS EN ISO 20346:2004, Personal protective equipment – Protective footwear;
☐	☐	☐	BS EN ISO 20347:2004, Personal protective equipment – Occupational footwear;
☐	☐	☐	BS EN ISO 21281:2005, Construction and layout of pedals of self-propelled sit-down rider-controlled industrial trucks – Rules for the construction and layout of pedals;
☐	☐	☐	BS EN 24869-1:1993 (ISO 4869-1:1990), Acoustics – Hearing protectors – Sound attenuation of hearing protectors – Subjective method of measurement;
☐	☐	☐	BS EN 29367-2:1995 (ISO 9367-2:1994), Lashing and securing arrangements on road vehicles for sea transportation on RO/RO ships – General requirements – Semi-trailers;
☐	☐	☐	BS EN 60079, Electrical apparatus for explosive gas atmospheres (all parts);
☐	☐	☐	BS EN 60598-2-25:1995 (IEC 60598-2-25:1994), Luminaires – Particular requirements – Luminaires for use in clinical areas of hospitals and health care buildings;
☐	☐	☐	BS EN 60695-4:2006, Fire hazard testing – Terminology concerning fire tests for electrotechnical products;
☐	☐	☐	BS EN 60745-1:2003, Hand-held motor-operated electric tools – Safety – General requirements;
☐	☐	☐	BS EN 60950-1:2002, Information technology equipment – Safety – General requirements;
☐	☐	☐	BS EN 61252:1997 (IEC 61252:1993), Electroacoustics – Specifications for personal sound exposure meters;
☐	☐	☐	BS EN 61285:2004, Industrial-process control – Safety of analyser houses;

	1	2	3	
	❏	❏	❏	BS EN 61310-1:1995 (IEC 61310-1:1995), Safety of machinery – Indication, marking and actuation – Requirements for visual, auditory and tactile signals;
	❏	❏	❏	BS EN 61310-2:1995 (IEC 61310-2:1995), Safety of machinery – Indication, marking and actuation – Requirements for marking;
	❏	❏	❏	DD CLC/TS 62081:2002, Arc welding equipment – Installation and use.

Bibliography

[1]   HSE (2001) *Reducing risks, protecting people: HSE's decision-making process*, Sudbury: HSE Books

[2]   HSE (2007) INDG417, Institute of Directors and Health and Safety Commission: *Leading health and safety at work – leadership actions for directors and board members*, Sudbury: HSE Books

[3]   HSE (1997) HSG65, *Successful health and safety management*, Sudbury: HSE Books

[4]   ILO (2001) ILO-OSH 2001, *Guidelines on occupational health and safety management systems*, Geneva: International Labour Office

[5]   BSI (2006) PAS 99:2006, *Specification of common management system requirements as a framework for integration*, London: British Standards Institution

[6]   HSE (2000) *Management of health and safety at work. Management of Health and Safety at Work Regulations 1999. Approved Code of Practice and guidance* L21 (second edition), Sudbury: HSE Books

[7]   Robens, Lord. (1972), *Safety and Health at Work: Report of the Committee 1970–72*, Cmnd 5034, London: HMSO

[8]   FRC (2006) *The Combined Code on Corporate Governance*, London: Financial Reporting Council

[9]   HSE (2005) *Control of Substances Hazardous to Health. The Control of Substances Hazardous to Health Regulations 2002. Approved Code of Practice and Guidance* L5 (fifth edition), Sudbury: HSE Books

[10]   HSE (2006) *Essentials of health and safety at work*, Sudbury: HSE Books

[11]   BCF (2001), *Code of Safe Practice: Application of Powder Coatings by Electrostatic Spraying*, Leatherhead: The British Coatings Federation

[12] HSE (2002) INDG261(rev1), *Pressure systems – safety and you*, Sudbury: HSE Books

[13] HSE (2002) HSG231, *Working safely with metalworking fluids. Good practice manual*, Sudbury: HSE Books

[14] HSE (1986) PM56, *Noise from pneumatic systems*, Sudbury: HSE Books

[15] HSE (2006) INDG163(rev2), *Five steps to risk assessment*, Sudbury: HSE Books

[16] HSE (2000) HSG202, *General ventilation in the workplace*, Sudbury: HSE Books

[17] HSE *Health and Safety Climate Survey Tool*, Sudbury: HSE Books

[18] BSI (2003) Carter, N, BIP 2006:2003, *Auditing the ISO 19011 Way*, London: British Standards Institution

[19] BSI (2003) IMS Risk Solutions Ltd, BIP 2011:2003, *Continual Improvement through Auditing (Integrated Management Systems Series)*, London: British Standards Institution

[20] BSI (2007) Smith, D and Politowski, R, BIP 2119:2007, *IMS: A framework for integrated management systems. Background to PAS 99 and its application (Integrated Management Systems Series)*, London: British Standards Institution